MIGRATING LEGACY SYSTEMS

GATEWAYS, INTERFACES & THE INCREMENTAL APPROACH

The Morgan Kaufmann Series in Data Management Systems

Series Editor, Jim Gray

MIGRATING LEGACY SYSTEMS

GATEWAYS, INTERFACES & THE INCREMENTAL APPROACH

MICHAEL L. BRODIE
MICHAEL STONEBRAKER

MORGAN KAUFMANN PUBLISHERS, INC.
SAN FRANCISCO, CALIFORNIA

INFORMATION TECHNOLOGY

EXECUTIVE EDITOR   Bruce M. Spatz
PRODUCTION MANAGER   Yonie Overton
ASSISTANT EDITOR   Douglas Sery
TECHNICAL EDITOR   Julie Pabst
COVER AND TEXT DESIGN/COMPOSITION   Rebecca Evans & Associates
ICON DESIGN   Carrie English, Canary Studios; Rebecca Evans & Associates
PROOFREADER   Jeff Van Bueren
INDEXER   Steve Rath
PRINTER   Bradford & Bigelow, Inc.

MORGAN KAUFMANN PUBLISHERS, INC.
Editorial and Sales Office
340 Pine Street, Sixth Floor
San Francisco, CA 94104-3205
USA
Telephone 415/392-2665
Facsimile 415/982-2665
Internet   mkp@mkp.com

Library of Congress Cataloging-in-Publication Data

Brodie, Michael L.
    Migrating legacy systems : gateways, interfaces & the incremental
approach / Michael L. Brodie, Michael Stonebraker.
        p.   cm.
    Includes bibliographical references and index.
    ISBN 1-55860-330-1
    1. Management information systems.   2. Software maintenance-Management.
I. Stonebraker, Michael. II. Title.
T58.6.B766   1995
004'.36—dc20   95-19699
                                                      CIP

To our children, Justin Brodie-Kommit and Sandra and Leslie Stonebraker

May their legacy enrich their future

FOREWORD

For the last five years, GTE Telephone Operations has been engaged in a massive effort to migrate from a legacy application environment that is characterized by hundreds of millions of lines of mainframe COBOL code and many tera-bytes of data. The data in these legacy systems are very much "owned" by the applications, with no sharing between applications. Redundant storage of information, captive to the applications, has led to excessive operations costs. We have employees whose only job is to fix data discrepancies.

Four years ago, GTE Telephone Operations began a huge effort to reengineer 80% of its business processes. This project was necessary as competition in the telephone industry is now becoming a reality. In addition, regulatory bodies are moving away from rate-of-return regulation and toward price-cap regulation. These facts sent a clear message: GTE needed to get its costs into competitive shape. Our legacy applications were the major impediment to implementing the new business processes.

Like many other enterprises, we moved quickly toward distributed, client/server, open systems computing. This technology allowed us to reuse legacy functionality while "surrounding" the legacy applications with new automated business processes, along with productivity-enabled graphical user interfaces. In addition, subject databases were architected to facilitate the sharing of common data, thereby eliminating redundancies and data discrepancies. At this point in time, we have successfully deployed several new automated business processes approaching 10,000 workstations. We still have a long way to go.

Our migration approach follows Chicken Little, the migration methodology described in this book. It will take us many years to fully migrate all of the legacy functionality to the client/server computing platforms, as we are migrating through carefully planned incremental steps. With 22 million telephone customers, we have to migrate our systems in such a way that zero downtime is virtually guaranteed. Thus each step is carefully calculated to minimize risks to the ongoing business processes. This is very much like overhauling an airplane, carrying a full load of passengers, in midflight.

There are many challenges remaining, most having to do with the inability of the mainframe to participate in distributed, client/server computing. For example, how do we provide transactional integrity when CICS is not capable of cooperating as a nested subtransaction in a client-initiated global transaction?

Had this book been available when we started the legacy IS migration journey, it would have been required reading for all of our systems planners and architects. This book provides an orderly methodology for beginning to clean up the mess that has taken us decades to make. It represents the first formal treatment of a subject that previously could be called "arts and crafty." And until now, frankly, it hasn't been one of the glamorous subjects that attracts the attention of research talent.

There are many migration approaches that have failed and few that have worked. This book provides a systematic approach to analyzing the current situation and making informed plans for getting to the new vision, thus delivering a higher probability of success. My thanks to Michael Brodie and Michael Stonebraker for their interest and contributions to a subject that has long needed attention.

Blayne Maring
Assistant Vice President, Technology Specifications
GTE Telephone Operations
Irving, Texas

Contents

PREFACE

ABOUT LEGACY IS MIGRATION

Legacy ISs are increasingly acknowledged as major problems for most large corporations. A legacy IS is any IS that significantly resists modification and change. Typically a legacy IS is big, with millions of lines of code, and more than 10 years old. But a legacy IS doesn't always fit this stereotype. If your IS was recently developed but cannot be readily modified to adapt to your constantly changing business requirements, it is a legacy.

If your legacy IS can't support your current business requirements, your business won't be able to remain competitive for long. If that isn't enough to get your attention, think of all the money and person-hours monopolized by legacy IS maintenance. It generally takes 80-90% of the IT budget and a considerable measure of pure luck, not to mention long-term operations staff who know the IS better than anyone else, just to keep the legacy IS running. And keep it running they must, since it is mission-critical, often operating 24 hours a day. If it's not the cost, it's the technical challenges that prevent action. For example, how can you modify the IS while it continues to perform its mission-critical function? No business will risk a failure that will lose the company time, business, and consumer confidence. And yes, the long-term operations staff who keep the legacy ISs running are often the first out the door at reengineering/downsizing time.

The commonsense solution to the legacy problem is migration. Over the past 10 years, there has been considerable discussion and publication on legacy IS migration. We have heard many claims that such migrations are being planned or are in progress. However, we have discovered only a handful of successful legacy IS migrations, worldwide. It's clear that legacy IS migration is a vastly more complex and costly process than anyone anticipates. A comprehensive plan is necessary to understand and handle the complexity of the migration process.

This book provides that plan. Our strategy is a viable solution for modifying legacy ISs into modern ISs that will support current business needs and adapt to future needs. We provide a supporting methodology, outline the technical challenges that arise, and identify tools needed to support the plan.

Our strategy is an incremental approach. That way you can keep your legacy running as you gradually migrate to the target environment. Management is likely to accept this proposition, primarily because it permits the control of risk. Management may also accept the notion because it leverages and protects the legacy; it is phased; and, it may be argued, it is cheaper than a complete rewrite. Moreover, users and developers are likely to accept the idea because it allows for a period of gradual adjustment.

We define a successful legacy IS migration as follows. It begins with a mission-critical, legacy IS of a significant size, in full production. It ends with a fully operational, mission-critical target application (or applications components) that replaces the essential aspects of the original legacy IS. Further, the target IS must contain significant content (primarily data but possibly application modules) from the migrated-and probably modified and augmented in the process-legacy IS. The target IS must be built using modern technology in place of legacy technology such as a legacy database service. For practical reasons, the target IS may contain legacy components for which there was not an adequate justification for their migration. However, the mission-critical functions and data that will live on must have been migrated.

Incremental migration is the only way to go. The alternative, a flash cut to a newly developed target system-what we call Cold Turkey-is simply infeasible for most large-scale, mission-critical ISs. Flash cuts have been the traditional answer. However, the complexity, size, and interoperation requirements of today's ISs make Cold Turkey impossible in all but the rarest cases. Many large-scale databases cannot be downloaded into a target database in the downtime permitted for a mission-critical application. And that does not take into account the necessary data scrubbing, transformation, integration steps, and so on. It is highly unlikely that a single target IS could be flash cut into operation without significantly affecting many other ISs that critically depend on the legacy IS and all its idiosyncrasies.

Ironically, the complexity of today's environments makes Cold Turkey infeasible, yet it also encourages people to consider Cold Turkey. It is so complex to consider how to incrementally migrate a legacy IS that planners often avoid the challenge altogether. They naively hope that Cold Turkey can handle it. Just do the numbers. If your planners suggest that Cold Turkey will work, we suggest that you look deeper.

THE CHICKEN LITTLE APPROACH

In this book we offer an incremental, 11-step migration approach that we call Chicken Little. Step by step, the legacy IS is migrated to the target environment. This allows you to control the risk involved. With our incremental strategy, you can determine the size of each chunk of the legacy IS migration. If a step fails, only the failed step need be repeated, not the entire project. Your company will realize gradually increasing benefits over time, culminating with a completed migration.

The 11 steps are flexible and adaptable. You can customize them to fit the needs of your legacy and of your organization. The steps don't have to proceed in order, they can be combined, or you may find that you can skip a few. Furthermore, it is entirely likely that before the migration of a large legacy IS is complete, unanticipated requirements will arise for further migration and evolution. Our strategy supports continuous evolution. Business reengineering can take place in conjunction with the IS migration. As new IS components are introduced, new ways of doing business may be incorporated into the organization, all with an eye toward future flexibility.

Future IS technology should support continuous, incremental evolution. IS migration is not a process with a beginning, middle, and end. Continuous change is inevitable. Current requirements rapidly become outdated, and future requirements cannot be anticipated. The primary challenge facing IS and related support technology is the ability to accommodate change (e.g., in requirements, operation, content, function, interfaces, and engineering).

IS evolution and migration must be considered dominant factors in IS life cycles. When ISs cost hundreds of millions of dollars and are mission-critical for business processes that have values in orders of magnitude greater, it is sheer folly to do otherwise. An appropriately designed target IS architecture can facilitate future evolution and integration with other ISs. If the target IS in not appropriately designed, it will become a next-generation legacy IS to be migrated at additional cost.

Database technology introduced the concept of data independence, whereby any changes to the database are isolated from the applications, and vice versa. The goal of data independence is the ability to change the database without affecting the applications, or to change the applications without affecting the database. Here we extend the concept of data independence to other components of ISs. Our goals are to achieve application independence, user interface independence, and IS interface independence. That way, each component of the IS can be modified independently to meet ever-changing requirements and to take advantage of new technologies. Obviously we can't prevent future legacies because we can't anticipate future business requirements or technology advances. But if you design your target IS to be completely decomposable (i.e., composed of separate components for each separable function), you'll be able to modify those components that do not support current needs when the time comes.

The critical success factor, and challenge in deployment, is proper identification of those functions that can be built using separable components. This is becoming the key software (and hardware) design challenge. This challenge underlies the current inability to design for reuse. We view this as the modern manifestation of the software crisis that was defined in 1969.

It takes planning and management to achieve an incremental migration that is feasible according to the technical and business requirements of your company. We've found that the migration process is greatly eased through the use of appropriate architectures, gateways, and other tools. Transparent interoperability provided by an environment consisting of these components supports the continuous evolution that we anticipate being the status quo.

We hope that in reading this book you will understand the simple principles behind our migration strategy, the sometimes complex technical requirements associated with the strategy, what you must expect of tools and environments that purport to support legacy IS migration, learn from the mistakes and successes in our case studies, and apply the knowledge to your particular needs. If your organization is currently planning to conduct a legacy IS migration, we further hope that our book and ideas will help you develop a successful migration plan. IS migration can be a massive undertaking with not a lot of understanding, successful experience, adequate tools, environments, or methodologies.

USING THIS BOOK

Our strategy is based on approximately 50 years of accumulated experience, an extensive background in databases and large-scale ISs legacy and new, and two case studies of planning and partially conducting legacy IS migration for very large-scale, mission-critical legacy ISs. We developed the migration plans for two major, multimillion-dollar corporations, here referred to as Money Central and Global Telecom. In this book, we address complex, large-scale ISs (e.g., millions of lines of code). However, the methodology is applicable, depending on requirements, to a wide range of ISs. As current ISs increasingly interact, even small ISs become part of a corporate IS environment. Hence, small ISs can gain the requirements of large-scale ISs, at least for the purposes of migration.

The migration plan of one case study has been expanded to encompass the entire corporate computing environment in support of the company's extensive reengineering plan. The plan includes a migration architecture, now extended to become a CORBA-like corporate computing architecture; gateways, now being constructed on a grand scale to support the migration of all corporate data into enterprise data servers; transaction support; interface gateways extended to establish a corporate-wide interface standard independent of specific applications; and a wide range of tools to support all aspects of application and data design, development, and migration. Indeed, the plan we developed of continuous migration and evolution is becoming the way this company uses IT to support its business.

Object orientation is addressed separately from the methodolgy, in Chapter 8. It was not originally considered in the case studies. However, it has now become a key enabling technology in both projects. Object orientation is rapidly becoming a real alternative to conventional languages and designs. The migration and target IS architectures are consistent with object orientation because of the principles underlying their design. First, they are distributed, client/server architectures. Second, all components are intended to be separable (e.g., encapsulated) modules that are defined and used by other components in terms of interface functions or methods. Third, the gateways and architecture can and should-regardless of the use of object orientation-facilitate communication between components by some form of message passing.

The methods and case studies presented in this book concern migrating legacy data and tossing legacy code. That is, we propose incremental rewriting of legacy applications as opposed to slicing and dicing legacy code for reuse in the target environment. However, because of the high cost and low benefit of migrating some legacy IS components, it can be optimal to leave these portions of legacy ISs untouched. They should be integrated transparently into the target distributed IS. Again, gateways, wrappers or adapters, are the primary means of achieving interoperability.

PLACING CHICKEN LITTLE IN CONTEXT

This book deals largely with the technical aspects of migration: how you carve up a legacy IS and migrate it piece by piece to a new environment. The book does not substantially address planning activities and organizational issues or how to incorporate a legacy IS migration into the enterprise view or architecture of the company. Because it is not our area of expertise, we have deliberately excluded discussion of the business aspects of migration. For example, determining business needs, assuring user buy-in, and so on, has been left to experts in those areas. However, we recognize that IT exists to support business requirements. Without that connection, IT does not address the real needs of the company.

Reengineering often views its target in terms of the desired business process. For example, a new business process for telecommunications service provisioning in Global Telecom is well understood since it has just been designed by the reengineering team. The "legacy" business process for business as usual is often not well documented or understood since it has evolved over many years and is instantiated in many locations by many people. Figure A illustrates this in the upper half, labeled *Business Process*. The challenge from the business perspective is to migrate from the legacy business processes to the target. Note here that IT does not enter into this business plan for the migration.

Figure A illustrates that the legacy business processes are supported at the information systems level by a complex arrangement of legacy ISs, and that the target business processes will be supported by some idealized target computing environment. That challenge-at that information systems level of migrating from the legacy ISs to the target ISs-is the topic of this book. It is critical to understand that the migration tasks are placed in a business context and in support of business requirements. The planning and execution of the legacy IS migration must be done in the context of the business process reengineering plan and requirements.

There is, however, a corresponding requirement from the information systems level to the business process level. The legacy IS cannot be migrated overnight. Hence, the speed of the business process migration must be consistent with what is feasible in terms of the legacy IS migration. At any point in the migration, the IS environment consists of a composite IS consisting of those components that have been migrated to the target and those that have not, the remaining legacy components. This is illustrated in Figure B. Correspondingly, the business process supported at that time is the combination of those processes supported by the composite IS, also illustrated in Figure B. This stunning observation indicates perhaps the most significant factor in determining which legacy component increments to migrate, a significant challenge mentioned above and throughout the book.

The business process migration may require that a certain feature be offered by a given milestone. Such milestones may determine the sequence of legacy increments to migrate. Alternatively, the cost or challenges related to migrating a particular increment may require that the business process migration be altered to be feasible. Hence, we claim that the business and IS levels are strongly interdependent. In this book, we focus on the technical aspects at the information systems level.

CHAPTER ORGANIZATION AND OVERVIEW

In Chapter 1, we describe legacy IS characteristics and introduce our 11-step migration strategy. Chapter 2 applies the 11 steps to decomposable IS architectures. We introduce the first case study in Chapter 3. This legacy IS fits the prototype of a decomposable IS. We demonstrate how the methods introduced in Chapter 2 can be applied to an actual IS. Chapter 4 tailors the 11-step strategy for migrating a semidecomposable IS architecture. Chapter 5 begins the discussion of the second case study. One portion of this IS is semidecompos-

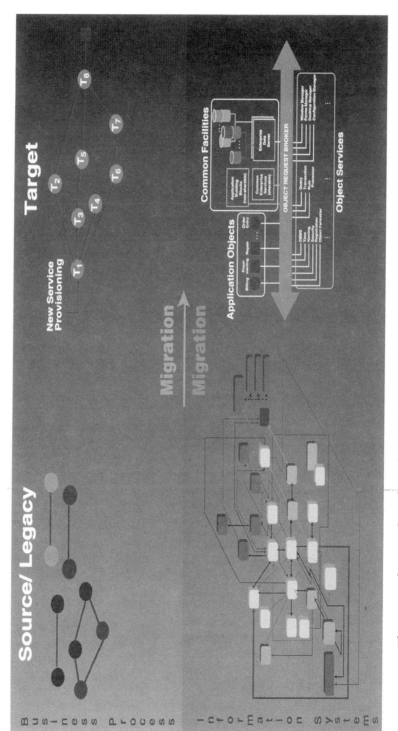

FIGURE A. The separate but interdependent relationship between legacy business process migration and legacy IS migration.

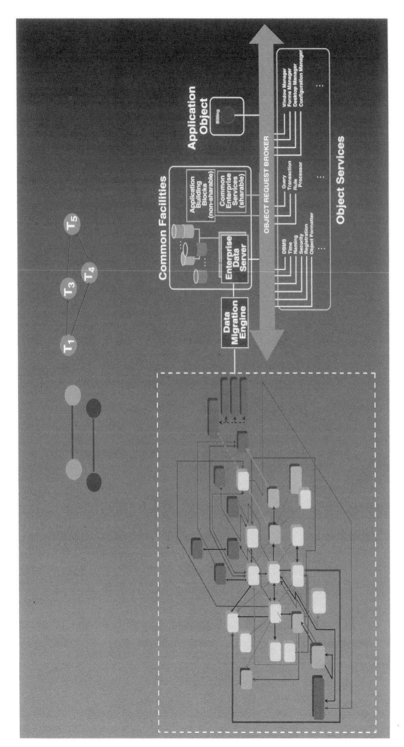

FIGURE B. A migration in process.

able, allowing us to apply methods of Chapter 4, and the other is portion is nondecomposable. In Chapter 6, we modify the 11 steps again, this time to migrate a nondecomposable IS. Chapter 7 combines the migration methods discussed previously to form a broadly applicable migration method. In Chapter 8, we talk about where IS design is headed. There are several possible directions, all of which permit Chicken Little. Chapter 9 is our tool wish list. We cover those areas where further tool development would be most helpful in Chicken Little legacy IS migration. Chapter 10, written by Jennifer Schmidt, provides information about existing tools. There's also a glossary with useful terms at the back of the book.

In Chapters 1 through 9, you'll frequently notice an acorn icon in the text margins. The acorn appears wherever we mention migration tools. Although tools are discussed throughout the book, they are covered in detail in Chapter 10. The acorn was designed to direct you to Chapter 10. If, as you're reading a particular chapter, you see the icon and decide that you'd like additional information about how tools can help you in the migration process, please turn to Chapter 10.

ACKNOWLEDGMENTS

It is with great pleasure that we acknowledge the many, valuable contributions to our understanding of the complex challenges and potential solutions to legacy IS migration. We have pursued this topic over many years and have learned a great deal from many people. We can list only a few here. For their contributions we thank, from GTE, Dale Beckham, Laurette Bradley, Sandy Heiler, Karen Huff, Chuck Karashin, George Kocur, Frank Manola, Blayne Maring, and Wes Oetinger. From the Money Central migration study we thank Jaime Carbonell, Carnegie Mellon University; John Davis, Anderson Consulting; Paula Hawthorn, Illustra Information Technologies, Inc.; Lawrence Markosian, Reasoning Systems; Sal Stolfo, Columbia University; and Robert Wilensky, University of California. From the research and industrial communities we thank Phil Bernstein, Microsoft Corporation; Bernd Bruegge, Carnegie Mellon University; Jim Gray, independent consultant; Ivar Jacobson, Objective Systems AB; Leonid Kalinichenko, Academy of Sciences of Russia; James Kirkley III, Digital Equipment Corporation; and Rene Miller, Ohio State University.

We would also like to thank the following for their reviews and very helpful comments: Robert Arnold, Software Evolution Technology; R. G. G. Cattell, SunSoft; Mark Crego, Legacy Solutions; Herbert Edelstein, Euclid Associates; J. C. Freytag, Digital Equipment Corporation; and Jim Gray. We thank Jennifer Schmidt for contributing Chapter 10, an important discussion of tools that makes the book more concrete to those who need to start immediately.

Finally, we would like to thank our editors at Morgan Kaufmann: Bruce Spatz, who had the vision and energy to make the book happen, and Julie Pabst, who put it all together and made sure that human beings could read the book and benefit from it. Julie added immensely to the content and flow of the book.

We thank you all for your contributions and friendship.

Chapter 1

PROBLEMS AND POSSIBILITIES OF LEGACY IS MIGRATION

Legacy information systems are a dominant concern of CIOs, strategic IS planners, and other corporate decision makers. Their maintenance is the sole activity of the vast majority of IS staff. Not only do legacy systems fall far short of current business requirements, they resist almost all necessary change. On one hand, they eat up CIOs' budgets. On the other, they provide the greatest opportunity to lower costs and improve the business.

There are only a couple of problems. The first is to keep the ISs running. The business depends on them. The second is to modify them to meet current business needs. This book addresses both problems. Modification inevitably requires replacement, but replacement will not work for large, mission-critical information systems. We offer an effective method to incrementally migrate ISs from their legacy environments and technologies, while they are still fully operational. The goal is a smooth migration path from inflexible, difficult-to-maintain, and easily breakable systems to ones that use the most appropriate and robust advanced technologies. That way the majority of the current deficiencies can be overcome.

Legacy IS problems may pose the most serious technical crises facing the IS staffs of corporate and governmental America. Reengineering demands modification that, in many cases, must be made in incremental steps. Many IS organizations feel as if they are on the edge of an enormous precipice that is about to crumble under the weight of the legacy. Tremendous technological strides have been made in hardware, software, and communications realms, yet how do you take advantage of it? We'll show you how.

We have developed a methodology that deals with all types of legacy ISs, from the largest to the smallest, the oldest to the newest, and the least structured to the most structured. Perhaps the characteristics of your legacy environment are exemplified by tens of millions of lines of COBOL and assembler code spread over hundreds of mainframe-based applications. Alternatively, perhaps you have recently developed C or C++ applications on a smaller scale that represent a legacy system in the making, posing difficult maintainability and infrastructure evolution before too many years pass. Our methodology is tailorable to both ends of this difficulty spectrum, as well as all points in between.

This book addresses the technical aspects of legacy IS migration. Simplifying and thus improving the technology are critical to any business reengineering process. However, we want to stress something: the technology is not and never should be the driving factor of reengineering a business. Business requirements are what drive technology or IS change.

Reengineering requires cooperation and understanding between the business management and technology management. Once business management has determined its goals, technology management must seek ways to modify the technology to support these goals. Our incremental strategy will help you do this. Each incremental change to the technology puts the business closer to maximum productivity.

1.1 THE LEGACY IS PROBLEM

Too many large organizations are mired in their IS sins of the past. Over 30 years of centralized, mainframe-oriented development—together with system and application development models, underlying hardware and software technologies, user interface paradigms (e.g., batch processing, dumb terminals), and other attributes of ISs—have brought most multinational companies, all levels of government organizations, and even a sizable portion of smaller organizations to a collective crisis point.

A *legacy information system* is any information system that significantly resists modification and evolution to meet new and constantly changing business requirements. Legacy ISs share many negative characteristics. Some of the worst, and lamentably typical, characteristics are the following:

> A legacy information system is any information system that significantly resists modification and evolution.

- Legacy ISs are large, with millions of lines of code.

- They're geriatric, often more than 10 years old.

- They're written in a legacy language like COBOL.

- They're built around a legacy database service (e.g., IBM's IMS). Sometimes they don't use a DBMS at all. Instead, the legacy IS is based on flat-file structures of ISAM, VSAM, or other file systems.

- Legacy ISs are autonomous. Applications operate independently, with little or no interface with other applications. If interfaces are present, they are often haphazard at best (e.g., based around export/import models or lacking in data consistency).

To complicate matters, these ISs are *mission-critical*—that is, essential to the organization's business—and must be operational at all times.

Organizations have outgrown their legacy ISs. The hardware for which the ISs were built is now inappropriate and antiquated. Applications are repeatedly patched, which means that maintenance is increasingly expensive and problematic. Often the patches, or emergency-oriented fixes, are unstructured and poorly controlled. This leads to situations where documentation is out-of-date and portions of source code don't exist. In addition, networking and communications infrastructures aren't "open" enough or don't provide adequate throughput to meet organizations' needs any more. What's more, business applications no longer sufficiently support current business processes. In any or all of these ways, legacy information systems present roadblocks to the full IS support of the corporate mission.

> Your legacy system keeps your business from staying on top.

Although the "classical" legacy IS is a mainframe-based, aging set of applications, it should be noted that the paradigm of legacy ISs is just as applicable to recently developed or constructed ISs that may involve midrange systems or even LAN-based technology. Increasingly expensive maintenance, prolonged delays in incorporating new functionality, and similar attributes may represent a legacy information system in the making. This is a problem that must be considered in the course of strategic IS planning. In short, most ISs today have the potential to degenerate into legacy systems possessing many of the negative characteristics just discussed.

1.2 MORE ABOUT LEGACY ISs

Migration from legacy IS environments is not an easy undertaking; in fact, it involves a great deal of cost, time, and effort. But it's important to realize that legacy IS problems can no longer be swept under the rug. The situation must be dealt with.

> Legacy system maintenance monopolizes your time and money.

Costs resulting from the problems of a single legacy IS, such as failures, maintenance, inappropriate functionality, lack of documentation, and poor performance, often exceed hundreds of millions of dollars per year. But legacy ISs are not only inordinately expensive to maintain. They are also *inflexible* and *brittle*. By inflexible, we mean that legacy systems are difficult to adapt to changing business needs. What's more, they are easily broken—brittle—when modified for any purpose.

There is a widespread fear that legacy ISs will soon break beyond repair. This fear, combined with a lack of techniques or technology to fix legacy IS problems, results in what we call *IS apoplexy*. It's easy to understand. The cost of maintaining and operating legacy ISs consumes at least 80% of the IS

Do you recognize this all too common story? It concerns a major information system that we consider later in the book as a case study of our migration methodology. This mission-critical IS has been fretted about for decades. It costs hundreds of millions of dollars a year to run. There is effectively no documentation except the code itself, which is written in a collection of little-used languages and runs on a proprietary operating system and obscure mainframe. Moreover, the original designers and developers have long since retired. The business model on which the IS was based no longer exists, and the primary business processes that it implements were terminated long ago. But performance is quite adequate, and the data is mission-critical.

The IS is operational 24 hours a day through the heroic efforts of a dedicated team of field operators. It has been augmented, patch by patch, for over 20 years. Now we've heard that two major enhancements are about to be cut over to the system. This news comes after several corporate edicts to terminate all enhancements.

Enhancements were to end for several reasons. First, there are plans to migrate following the methods described in this book. New developments were to be directed toward the target information system, not the legacy. Second, enhancements further complicate the already tremendous maintenance problems. As it is, a significant library of programs has been created to help find errors in the data that result from frequent system failures. This library was built to reduce the constant manual intervention still necessary to keep this massive legacy IS running.

budget, but more often up to 90–95%. This prevents organizations from moving to newer software (such as that based around client/server configurations), current-generation DBMSs, and 4GLs. Consequently, organizations are prevented from *rightsizing*—moving from large mainframe computers to smaller, less expensive computers that fully meet current IS requirements. It is indeed ironic that the corporate and government organizations with larger IS budgets are often unable to take advantage of the same technological advances to the same degree as smaller or newer companies with a smaller embedded legacy system base.

This apoplexy, in turn, is a key contributor to the software crisis. New requirements, often called the *IS backlog*, cannot be met since legacy ISs can't be extended nor new ISs developed with the IS funds remaining. These problems are both key motivations of and major roadblocks to the worldwide movement to reengineer corporations and their major ISs. This irony becomes a major threat when aggressive and nimble start-ups with no legacy can develop or purchase information systems that take advantage of the most recent technologies to build flexible, efficient systems. These systems are able to meet immediate business requirements, then support changes when business requirements change.

| IS apoplexy may permit competitors to eat your lunch. |

The now-famous MCI "Friends and Family" advertising campaign, the most successful in the telecommunications industry to date, is based on the flexibility of MCI's billing systems. They use their modern billing system as a

---

Enhancements are made for all kinds of reasons—for example, to improve functionality, to increase performance, or to fix known problems. Some are large, such as those just mentioned, and some are small (e.g., midnight fixes by single programmers). The relatively small enhancements are made in order to achieve necessary changes supposedly quickly and simply, with little overhead, cost, and risk. These are all positive benefits, but they obscure the underlying problems. After all, a mountain of enhancements does not a reliable system make. They happen with little visibility and with little overall direction.

Experience often shows that combining a number of enhancements into a major enhancement significantly increases the risk of failure. Major changes require big budgets, long schedules, and the delivery of big paybacks, at least commensurate with the resource consumption. They naturally raise expectations based on the promises that the proposers were forced to present. Everything—budget, schedule, programming team—seems to add up to be much more than the sum of the parts. All for the supposed benefit of systematizing a collection of enhancements.

It is the major enhancements that produce IS apoplexy in management, since the costs and risks seem too great for the benefits. We propose a methodology based on relatively small enhancements, or, as we call them, migration steps, since they are more doable both technically and in terms of expense and near-term payback than a large, major enhancement. Yet each step contributes to achieving a global plan.

5

corporate weapon against their competitors. MCI has launched many new programs, such as providing discounts to customers who frequently call the same numbers, that are largely new ways of billing customers. In so doing, MCI uses its IS flexibility to set the business agenda and to gain market share while competitors struggle with their legacy or develop new systems to bypass their legacy. In this case, AT&T could not add new function to their billing system because of its legacy nature. The point is, IS apoplexy may permit competitors to eat your lunch.

1.3 THE SOLUTION: MIGRATION

The commonsense solution to the problems of legacy systems is a migration program. This involves replacing problematic hardware and software, including the interfaces, applications, and databases that currently compose an IS infrastructure with newer, more modern hardware and software.

One of the problems common to many organizations is a close binding of the IS applications with associated data assets. This characteristic, arguably a necessity in the days of file-based information management, has stubbornly persisted throughout the years, even as DBMS products and database environments have become more and more common in organizations. Part of the reason is that a sizable portion of corporate and government data assets is still contained within file systems—a property that indicates the resistance of legacy systems to change.

> Close binding of the IS applications with associated data assets is a common problem.

An organization can greatly increase control over the IS by incorporating a modern DBMS with facilities for backup, recovery, transaction support, efficient query, and increased data independence (as well as performance improvements over its file system and early DBMS ancestors) into the *target environment*. This is the hardware and software that will be the new host environment for the post-migration system. Maintenance of the system becomes easier because of the increased amount of work done by off-the-shelf systems software rather than custom-developed routines. More importantly, modern DBMS usage also provides a basis for future evolution and integration with other ISs. This is commonly referred to as *enterprise computing*. For example, a DBMS could facilitate *data liberation*. Any application could use the DBMS to access valuable corporate data that is currently inaccessible because of the legacy database service that encapsulates it. As we'll discuss throughout this book, *the successful migration of the data management service from the legacy to the target is the key to overcoming many of the problems discussed in the previous section*. But before we go any further, we need to clarify what we mean by migration.

1.4 ABOUT THE TERM MIGRATION

Almost everyone with a legacy IS must maintain and adapt it to meet new logical and physical requirements, or to just keep it running. Indeed, the vast majority of IS labor and tools deal with legacy IS evolution and maintenance. Since legacy ISs are always being modified into something new, you might consider this to be a migration of sorts, from the legacy IS to its new IS. However, we do not include maintenance and evolution, in this sense, in our definition of legacy IS migration.

> Legacy IS migration begins with a legacy IS and ends with a comparable target IS.

Legacy IS migration, as we consider it here, involves starting with a legacy IS and ending with a comparable target IS. This target IS is significantly different from the original, but it contains substantial functionality and data from the legacy IS. A common example is migrating a legacy IS from a mainframe environment to a client/server environment. Or a legacy IS could be migrated from one technology (e.g., files and COBOL) to another (e.g., relational DBMS and 4GL). The case studies in this book focus on migrating from a mainframe and non-DBMS-based legacy IS to an IS that is based on client/server, relational DBMSs, and 4GLs. In later chapters we consider distributed computing and object-orientation as target technologies. We consider true migrations ones of functionality (not code) and data (yes, legacy data). Much of the legacy application code is dispensable or replaceable; significant amounts of legacy data are not.

Almost all IS shops, labor, and tools in the world deal with legacy IS maintenance and evolution. But almost no one is actively migrating, and no comprehensive tools have been developed to aid legacy IS migration. Over the past five years, we have asked a large number of IS shops, CIOs, consulting organizations, and researchers around the world these questions: What is your experience with migrating legacy ISs? What large or small examples do you know? What problems were encountered? What were the effective solutions, tools, and strategies? Without exception, everyone recognized the significance and prevalence of the problem, but fewer than five had any experience with migration.

This seems odd given that client/server, reengineering, and reverse engineering topics have been so hotly discussed during recent years. Moreover, database and schema migration has been a topic of research papers for 20 years. It seems fairly obvious that these topics would include legacy IS migration. Indeed, this

> Two different companies planned migrations of their information systems to take place over a span of five to eight years. (Both of these migrations are presented later in the book as case studies.) Less than a year into the process, both companies halted the migration efforts in order to incorporate requirements that arose since the migration began. In both cases, the new requirements included the use of advanced technologies not originally planned (e.g., object orientation) and new corporate strategies (e.g., business process reengineering).

observation drove us to our first legacy IS migration exercise. We thought it was incredibly difficult, yet so many articles and discussions seemed to suggest successful client/server migrations. What we have found by pursuing such stories in detail is that there is virtually no migration involved. The target IS is almost always a completely new IS with new code and new data. Legacy IS function is rewritten, possibly after reverse engineering to understand the legacy IS code. Legacy IS data is sometimes migrated, but never in a comprehensive way. What's worse is that the newly generated IS is almost always developed in parallel with the legacy IS, and then operation is cut over to the newly generated IS. Many such projects have failed.

This strategy will simply not work anymore in all practical cases. We hope to demonstrate this point and champion an apparently new strategy, the incremental migration of legacy ISs, in the following section. Practically speaking, for all but the simplest ISs, there is no other alternative.

1.5   MIGRATION STRATEGIES

We've talked about how the consumption of IS resources by inefficient legacy systems maintenance often precludes the investment in new technology necessary to support long-term organizational productivity. This is a primary justification for pursuing complex, expensive migration programs that will affect much or all of an organization's IS environment. The investment and the diversion of personnel resources are necessary to overcome the paralyzing consumption of IS resources.

It's not enough, however, to merely proclaim that organizations should aggressively pursue migration programs with the intent of incorporating target environments built around modern, evolvable technologies. How such a program is tackled can have a tremendous impact on the success or failure of the effort.

There are two strategies for migrating legacy ISs:

- *Cold Turkey*
- *Chicken Little*

Let's look at each of these.

1.5.1   The Cold Turkey Approach

Some legacy IS addicts try to quit Cold Turkey. They attempt to rewrite the legacy IS from scratch to produce the target IS, using modern software techniques and the hardware of the target environment. This strategy carries substantial risk of failure for the following reasons.

1. A better system must be promised.

It is nearly impossible to propose a one-for-one rewrite of a complex IS. Management rarely budgets the required major expenditure if the only payoff is lower maintenance costs in the distant future. Additional business functions must be promised. This adds complexity to the replacement IS and increases the risk of failure.

2. Business conditions never stand still.

The development of large, complex ISs requires years to accomplish. While the legacy IS rewrite proceeds, the original legacy IS evolves in response to

- maintenance,
- urgent business requirements, and
- midnight functions (i.e., features installed by programmers in their spare time).

It is a significant problem to ensure that the developing replacement IS evolves in step with the evolving legacy IS.

More significant than maintenance and minor ad hoc changes are changes in the business processes that the IS is intended to support. These are typically in a constant state of flux. The prospect of incorporating support for new business processes in the replacement IS may lead to significant changes to the IS's requirements throughout its development. This also increases the risk of failure.

3. Specifications rarely exist.

The only documentation for legacy ISs is typically the code itself. The original implementors have long since departed.

We proposed a number of legacy IS migrations that were not approved by senior management. They understood the antiquity of the underlying business models and processes and refused to provide significant resources to reimplement them. They felt that the legacy systems should be discarded and new systems built to replace them. This led to some massive Cold Turkey failures that left the legacy ISs untouched, except for patches. Hence, the legacy ISs continued to support only the old business requirements. The refusal to fix the base legacy ISs further complicated the problem. Newly required functions and data typical of evolving business needs were incorporated in the legacy systems by patches and in other systems, legacy and new. This substantially broadened the scope of any future migration to a consolidated target IS.

COLD TURKEY IMPEDIMENTS

1. A better system must be promised.

2. Business conditions never stand still.

3. Specifications rarely exist.

4. Undocuments dependencies frequently exist.

5. Legacy ISs can be too big to cut over data.

6. Management of large projects is hard.

7. Lateness is seldom tolerated.

8. Large projects tend to bloat.

9. Homeostasis is prevalent.

10. Analysis paralysis sets in.

Let's continue the story we began earlier of the undocumented, mission-critical, massive legacy IS. Because of its size and lack of documentation, it is treated largely as a black box. However, understanding its function and data is critical for some activities—for example, migration, performance analysis and enhancements, functional enhancements, patches, or access of its mission-critical data. Over the years, many techniques and much effort have been invested to this end: interviewing users about its functions and data content, trapping all accesses to find the nature and patterns of usage, and yes, launching exploratory missions of National Geographic proportions into mountains and valleys of core dumps of code and data. And still, we know little. What we do find horrifies us. For example, we found that a "LOCATION-CODE" field had been used over the years for a street address, a building type, and—this was for more than a decade—the tax treatment of capital assets in the building. But in spite of these problems, the legacy IS goes on and on and on.

Documentation is often nonexistent, out-of-date, or lost. The original specifications and coding practices are now considered primitive or bad (e.g., self-modifying code).

For example, the code is often the only documentation for the commonplace *variant record* encodings, in which the interpretation of one data element is controlled by another data element. Often legacy code was written for high performance on some extinct computer, resulting in arcane code constructs.

In such situations, the exact function of the legacy IS must be decrypted from the code if it is to be understood or copied in the replacement IS. This adds greatly to the complexity and cost of developing the replacement IS.

4. Undocumented dependencies frequently exist.

Invariably, applications, from noncritical (e.g., reporting and other informational programs) to mission-critical, access the legacy IS for its mission-critical information and other resources. Over the 10-plus-year life of the typical legacy IS, the number of these dependent ISs grows. Their presence is rarely known to the legacy IS owners. If the legacy IS is to be rewritten from scratch, Cold Turkey strategists must identify and deal with these dependencies. This again adds to the complexity of the rewrite and raises the risk of failure of dependent ISs.

For the legacy information system in one of our case studies, we broadcast a company-wide memo that asked employees to identify any uses of the subject system that they depend on. To our immense surprise, we discovered 1,200 dependent applications that were not known beyond the users/developers of those programs. It made sense operationally, since the data is mission-critical. Most dependent applications were report writers and query programs. However, some were gateways to other mission-critical information systems. Modifying the legacy information system or even its interface may, through ripple effects, bring hundreds of apparently separate information systems and attendant business processes to their knees.

5. Legacy ISs can be too big to cut over data.

Many legacy ISs must be operational almost 100% of the time. Many legacy databases or files require weeks to dump or download. Even if the rewritten IS were fully operational, there are no techniques to migrate the live data from the legacy IS to the new IS within the time that the business can support being without its mission-critical IS. Live data must be not only cleaned or scrubbed but also converted to fit the new system, again increasing project time and complexity. This may not just add complexity, it often prohibits Cold Turkey altogether.

6. Management of large projects is hard.

The difficulty of most large projects is seriously underestimated. Hence, there is a tendency for them to grow uncontrollably in head count. Few organizations are capable of managing the development of an IS with the several hundred contributors that are common for ISs of the size and complexity we are considering. Managing more and more people inevitably brings on the famous *Brooks effect* (Brooks 1975). In his classic book, which is required reading for any serious computer scientist, Brooks describes experiences in which the addition of resources to late projects makes them even later. That is, the result is the opposite of the desired effect. Reasons for the Brooks effect include the necessity of repartitioning the work, the necessity of training new personnel, and the added complexity of the resulting human interactions.

7. Lateness is seldom tolerated.

Large projects are inevitably late because of the problems cited above. Management patience wears out quickly, especially in organizations whose basic function is not software production. This frequently results in the termination of partly or mostly completed projects. In one organization, a large project was several years late when it was terminated. The personnel involved who are still with the company have a cloud on their reputations to this day. When you consider the financial constraints and general budget-cutting philosophy

The databases and files used by the legacy information systems in our case studies would take weeks to download if the legacy data servers provided a download function. However, in most cases, the only way to access the legacy data is via the legacy IS itself. This would prolong the download to months instead of weeks. We don't know of any products that can economically overcome these problems, although the developers of some data scrubbing and translation products claim otherwise.

Legacy data migration is a critical business and technical problem, independent of legacy code migration. As we've said before, legacy code can be rewritten, but much of legacy data is mission-critical for day-to-day business operations.

A large-scale migration based on the methods in this book had, as an initial step, a platform migration involving no other change. By the time this step was canceled, it had acquired a management structure and budget all its own. It had a full-time director, a significant-sized team, a multimillion dollar budget, and some impressive milestones. After all, this pilot project, if it succeeded, would by necessity be duplicated throughout the organization. So the now-terminated project and division gained objectives far beyond the original intent. This greater scope made the project significantly late. It is likely that the budget became so inflated that it put the entire project at risk. Indeed, the budget was reallocated when management was looking for a large source of funds for a new mission-critical project and saw the project fall increasingly behind schedule.

pervasive in the corporate world today, it's easy to see how even a small series of developmental setbacks can lead to project (and personnel) termination.

8. Large projects tend to bloat.

There is a tendency for large projects to become bloated with nonessential groups. For example, for a project as critical as a legacy IS migration, organizations may want to explore the introduction of new management techniques and technologies (e.g., reengineering, CASE). This is often done by adding groups to the already large project. Groups that are not critical to the migration itself increase the budget and management complexity, thus making the project more vulnerable to failure and then termination.

9. Homeostasis is prevalent.

Fear of change, new techniques, and new technologies all contribute to enormous resistance to Cold Turkey migration. People don't want to think about or deal with the difficulties of this process. When the complexity and high risk of Cold Turkey threaten to unsettle their equilibrium, they'd rather make do with their ineffective but comfortable legacy. Homeostasis reduces the amount of cooperation your migration team will receive, and it severely hampers the project's chance for ultimate success.

Over the decades-long lives of the ISs considered in our case studies, many migrations or other major modifications have been attempted. In one case there have been over 25; in the other, more than 12. All have failed. To this day, the original systems exist largely unchanged, except for continuous, ad hoc patches. The primary resistance to change comes not from these legacy ISs but from the divisions responsible for the ISs. These organizations provide the major proponents of homeostasis and the heroic efforts to keep the ISs running. Reengineering America and the consequent shift of emphasis to business processes and away from ISs changes all this. Now CIOs need effective methods to migrate the legacy ISs. The remainder of this book outlines such a method.

10. Analysis paralysis sets in.

Cold Turkey migration cannot begin until you understand everything about your IS, or so it is often believed. But the system is so large and so convoluted that you can't possibly understand it all. So you analyze and analyze without ever migrating. Obviously Cold Turkey cannot succeed when the project can never begin.

Cold Turkey doesn't allow for a period of gradual adjustment and adaptation. What's more, Cold Turkey involves high risk. It has been applied and has failed many times in large organizations. In fact, one organization in the financial services sector has tried Cold Turkey on three occasions over the last 15 years on mission-critical legacy ISs, and it has failed each time. The total financial write-off of these failures exceeded $1 billion. This figure becomes even greater when you consider the cost of the lost opportunities to benefit from a more modern IS.

Let's now look at an alternative, lowest-risk, and novel strategy, Chicken Little, the focus and contribution of this book. Our methodology aims to achieve two goals.

- It deals with legacy IS problems and provides a path away from them.

- It establishes an IS infrastructure that helps prevent the problems from recurring.

1.5.2 The Chicken Little Alternative

When an acorn fell on his head, Chicken Little concluded that the sky was falling. From that point on, his driving purpose was to warn the king. Although we question Chicken Little's deductive powers, we admire his cautious, conservative character. These are valuable qualities, especially in legacy IS migration. We also understand Chicken Little's motivation: we must always keep the kingdom (business) running and meet the needs of the citizens (customers). A cautious, conservative approach aimed at keeping the business running and meeting customer needs is what forms the foundation of our migration method. That's why we've chosen to give Chicken Little some long-overdue recognition and name our strategy after him.

Chicken Little involves migrating the legacy IS, in place, by small incremental steps until the desired long-term objective is reached. Each step requires a relatively small resource allocation (e.g., a few person-years) and little time. It produces a specific, small result toward the desired goal—an *increment*. Hence, the Chicken Little approach is an *incremental migration methodology*.

As necessity and courage dictate, greater and greater risk could be incorporated into a Chicken Little migration program, with the form of that risk being larger increments. Chicken Little permits planners to control risk, step by step, by choosing the increment

---

THE CHICKEN LITTLE STRATEGY

Migrate the legacy IS, in place, by small incremental steps until the desired long-term objective is reached. Chicken Little permits planners to control risk, step by step, by choosing the increment size.

> Rome wasn't built in a day, and neither was AT&T.

size. The smaller the increment, the smaller the risk and the smaller the gain. But Rome was not built in a day, and neither was AT&T.

This is in sharp contrast to the vast resource requirements of a complete rewrite (hundreds of person-years), a multiyear development, and one massive result. If a Chicken Little step fails, only the failed step must be repeated, not the entire project. Since steps are designed to be relatively inexpensive, such incremental steps do not need to promise dramatic new function to get funded.

Each problem of the Cold Turkey approach cited in Section 1.5.1 can be addressed in an incremental fashion. In addition, failures in individual steps may indicate large or previously unforeseen problems. These problems in turn can be addressed incrementally. That's why Chicken Little is so much safer and more feasible than Cold Turkey. Table 1.1 provides a comparison of the two migration strategies.

	Cold Turkey	Chicken Little
Risk	Huge	Controllable
Failure	Entire project fails	Only one step fails
Benefits	Immediate, probably short-lived	Incremental, over time
Outlook	Unpredictable until deadline	Conservatively optimistic

TABLE 1.1 A comparison of Cold Turkey and Chicken Little.

In our discussion in the following chapters, we investigate and apply the Chicken Little migration strategy to various types of legacy ISs. The key to successful Chicken Little migration, and its principal challenge, concerns the selection of independent increments to migrate (i.e., portions of legacy interfaces, applications, and databases that can be transitioned independently of each other), the sequencing of the increments to achieve the desired goal, and dealing with unavoidable problems (e.g., dependencies between migration steps).

1.6 MIGRATION COMPLEXITY AND IS ARCHITECTURES

In addition to the choice of migration methodology, the complexity of the migration effort—and its likely success or failure—is affected by the IS architecture of the legacy environment.

An IS architecture reflects the solution to the particular IS problem. The total IS function is decomposed into a number of individual functions. Those functions are further decomposed into subfunctions, and so forth, forming a hierarchy of functions in what is called a functional decomposition of the IS. The IS is "architected" into components or modules that reflect this structure. A higher-level function has interfaces to lower-level functions that support its operation.

All ISs can be considered as having three components: 1) interfaces, 2) applications, and 3) a database service. The architectures of legacy ISs vary widely on a spectrum from well-structured (i.e., modular, hence decomposable into its component parts or modules) to unstructured (i.e., nondecomposable). The history of IS development is reflected in IS architectures. When ISs were first developed, they were not as complex as today's ISs. Not only were detailed decompositions not required, they were not yet conceived. As IS functionality became increasingly complex, they required more functional decomposition, thus prompting methods such as structured programming, which applied to programs or modules but not necessarily to data. As database management systems came into being in the 1960s and 1970s, modularity and sharing of data became more commonplace, but the actual use of the technology did not catch on in a big way until the 1980s. Still later, user interfaces came to be seen in a systematic way so that they too could be handled structurally.

The above notions of the separation of concerns and the decomposition of IS function as well as IS support technology (e.g., DBMSs) evolved over 30 to 40 years. This is reflected directly in the IS architectures developed over that period. So now, let's look briefly at the well-structured and unstructured extremes and one point in between.

1.6.1 Decomposable Legacy IS Architectures

The best architecture for migration purposes is a *decomposable structure*, in which the interfaces, applications, and database services can be considered as distinct components with well-defined interfaces. Figure 1.1 illustrates a decomposable legacy IS that consists of a collection of independent application modules, each interacting with a database service and each, potentially, with its own user interface and system interface, through which it interacts with one or more foreign ISs. Interfaces, both user and system, must be considered separately since they differ significantly in technology, design, performance requirements, and impact (e.g., number and requirements of human users versus ISs accessing the legacy IS).

For an architecture to be decomposable, the application modules must be independent of each other, that is, have no hierarchical structure, and interact *only* with the database service.

15

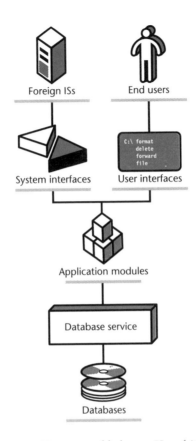

FIGURE 1.1 Decomposable legacy IS architecture.

1.6.2 Semidecomposable Legacy IS Architectures

A more difficult architecture with respect to migration purposes is a *semide-composable* legacy IS, illustrated in Figure 1.2. In contrast with a decomposable legacy IS, only user interfaces and system interfaces are separate modules. The applications and database service are *not* separable from one another since their structures are more complex, not adequately engineered in accordance with current standards, or poorly understood and thus can't be decomposed. The lack of desirable structure makes analysis and migration more complex and error-prone.

> Legacy architectures can be classified as decomposable, nondecomposable, or hybrid (containing decomposable and nondecomposable modules).

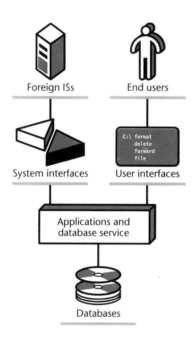

FIGURE 1.2 Semidecomposable legacy IS architecture.

1.6.3   Nondecomposable Legacy IS Architectures

The worst architecture for migration is a *nondecomposable* legacy IS, illustrated in Figure 1.3. Such ISs are, from a system point of view, black boxes since no functional components are separable. End users and ISs interact directly with one, apparently unstructured, component or module.

1.6.4   Discussion

Often the architecture of a legacy IS isn't strictly decomposable, semidecomposable, or nondecomposable. During its decades-long evolution, a legacy IS may have had parts added that fall into each architectural category, resulting in a *hybrid* architecture, as illustrated in Figure 1.4. As you can see in the figure, some interface and application modules are inseparable from the legacy database service, whereas others are modular and independent.

Your technical team must analyze the legacy IS architecture and consider the consequent complexity of the IS migration. Once you've determined what category your legacy architecture falls into, the migration plan can be tailored accordingly. Since the separable components are easier to deal with than those that are inseparable, the migration should take advantage of these benefits wherever possible. Although these variations add complexity to the architecture

17

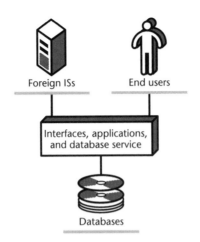

FIGURE 1.3 Nondecomposable legacy IS architecture.

and migration, they also provide potential benefits because separable components facilitate separate (i.e., incremental) migrations.

1.7 THE ROLE OF GATEWAYS

A Chicken Little legacy IS migration involves incrementally selecting and migrating parts of the legacy IS to become new parts of the incrementally constructed target IS. During the migration, the legacy IS and the target IS form a *composite IS*, which collectively provides the mission-critical IS function. In the composite IS, the legacy IS and target IS are connected by a *gateway*, as illustrated in Figure 1.5.

Gateways play the key role in the migration architectures described in this book. By gateway we mean a software module introduced between operational software components to mediate between them. Although communications gateways that promote internetwork and inter-protocol operability also play a role in migration methodologies, we limit our focus to the definition above. There are many commercial gateway products that possess some of the functionality required for our purposes. These are discussed in Chapter 10.

> ### GATEWAYS
>
> - Insulate certain components from changes being made to other components. Available gateway products perform this function.
> - Translate requests and data between the mediated components. Available gateway products perform this function to a limited degree.
> - Coordinate between mediated components for update consistency. Few commercial gateway products do this.

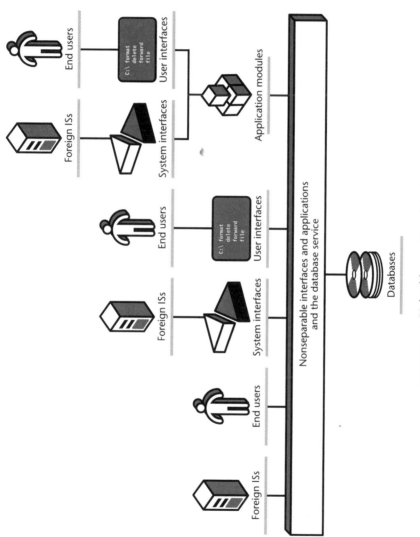

FIGURE 1.4 Hybrid legacy IS architecture.

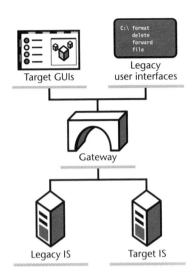

FIGURE 1.5 IS migration architecture.

Gateways have been used ever since Ada Lovelace coded two modules that had to interact. Given its controlling position, a gateway can mediate many things or play many roles. Some roles are easily understood and supported. Some roles have yet to be understood, let alone supported by commercial products.

One gateway role is to insulate certain components from changes being made to others. In Figure 1.5, the gateway makes any change to the legacy IS transparent to the legacy user interface. That is, the gateway maintains the interface that the user interface expects of the legacy IS, even though the legacy IS is being changed behind the scenes. This transparency permits you to alter one part of the legacy IS at a time. This capability is critical to the Chicken Little strategy. As the target graphical user interface in Figure 1.5 is incrementally introduced, the gateway makes transparent to both the graphical user interface and the user interface whether the legacy IS, target IS, or both are supporting a particular function. Hence, the gateway can insulate a component that is not being changed (e.g., the user interface) from components that are changing (e.g., migrating the legacy database to the target database).

A gateway also acts as translator of requests and data between the mediated components. For example, a gateway can translate calls from the user interface to the target IS, or data from the target IS to legacy user interface formats. This is the second major role of a gateway.

Gateways are widely used as mediators and translators. However, we know of only a few commercial gateway products that support the third critical function: coordination between the mediated components. There are two primary forms of access that must be coordinated: queries and updates. A query or update is sent to a logical collection of data. The data or the function that implements the query or update may be partially or fully decomposed in the source IS component and partially or fully migrated to target components. For various reasons, there may be multiple copies of data or function, further complicating the coordination. The gateway has to decompose the query or update appropriately so that it sends the appropriate subquery or subupdate to the right function and data. Coordinating queries requires that the single source query is decomposed, that the subqueries are sent to the appropriate components, and that the responses are collected and integrated to form a consistent single response. Subqueries against copies must be discounted or dealt with appropriately. The same is true of updates, but coordination is more complex. The end product of the update is that all components, especially copies, reflect the correct, single intended update. This requires advanced database technology called transaction management. Another detail is worth considering. Not all copies need to be precisely consistent. Some updates can be delayed, thus reducing the complexity of the update at the time of the update. For example, a master copy may require immediate update and secondary copies could be updated at a later time. Also, some data, such as prices, may require immediate update, while other data, such as historical data, can have updates deferred.

The importance is that *corresponding new and legacy copies of data may need to be consistent*. Because few gateway products ensure this, it must be done manually by staff. You, the decision maker in the migration process, may have to refuse gateway access for anything other than read-only query access until update consistency of your mission-critical data can be assured between your legacy and target environments. If you can't guarantee updates to your mission-critical data, then how long will that data be a correct reflection of your business?

This was a technical challenge to database technologists that took years to achieve. Update consistency across heterogeneous information systems is a much more complex technical problem with no general solution yet devised, and it is still an open research challenge. The only solution is to develop special-purpose applications, *once you understand the problems peculiar to each particular situation*.

The placement of the gateway is a critical factor that affects the complexity or simplicity of the migration architecture, the gateway, and the migration method. In the best case—the decomposable legacy IS—the gateway can be placed between the application modules and the legacy database service, illustrated in Figure 1.6 (a). In this case, we call it a *database gateway* since it encapsulates the entire database service and database from the perspective of the application modules.

For the semidecomposable legacy IS, the lowest the gateway can be placed is between the interfaces and the rest of the legacy IS (applications, database service, and database), illustrated in Figure 1.6 (b) and in Figure 1.5. It is called an *application gateway* because it encapsulates from the applications down, from the perspective of the interfaces. Because of the functionality it encapsulates, an application gateway can be considerably more complex than a database gateway. In general, the higher up in the architecture the gateway is placed, the more functionality it encapsulates and the greater its complexity.

Finally, an *IS gateway* encapsulates the entire legacy IS when you have a nondecomposable legacy IS, as illustrated in Figure 1.6 (c). Therefore, it is the most complex. The IS gateway is the primary means for dealing with the user interface. We describe this in more detail in Section 1.8. Indeed, because of the importance of user interface aspects, we recommend that IS gateways be used in all migrations.

Now that we've defined the types of gateways in terms of placement, we introduce the concept of two component parts of all gateways that are usable during a phased Chicken Little migration: *forward gateways* and *reverse gateways*. Both play an important role and must be used together during a migration effort.

A forward gateway enables legacy applications to access a database environment on the target side of the migration process, whereas a reverse gateway enables target applications to access the legacy data management environment. Forward gateways translate legacy (old technology) calls *forward* to target (new technology) calls. In contrast, reverse gateways translate target calls in the *reverse* direction back into legacy calls. Figure 1.7 illustrates both types of gateways.

Since change is constant and the migration process may take a long time, the gateway may serve future migration and evolution requirements. It may also be the case that legacy components may not undergo migration for economic or technical reasons. Hence, the gateway may be required as long as legacy and target components need to coexist. Also, subsequent migration may begin before the current migration completes. Subsequent migrations may require the gateway. Indeed, we believe that the composite IS architecture may become the permanent architecture to support continuous evolution.

1.8 INTERFACE MIGRATION

Interface migration is critical to both the end users and the external systems that interact with the composite IS. The legacy IS contains key corporate resources, and the user and system interfaces control all uses of the system and all access to those resources. Hence, IS interfaces are as critical to your business as the databases and the applications. Errors that originate in the

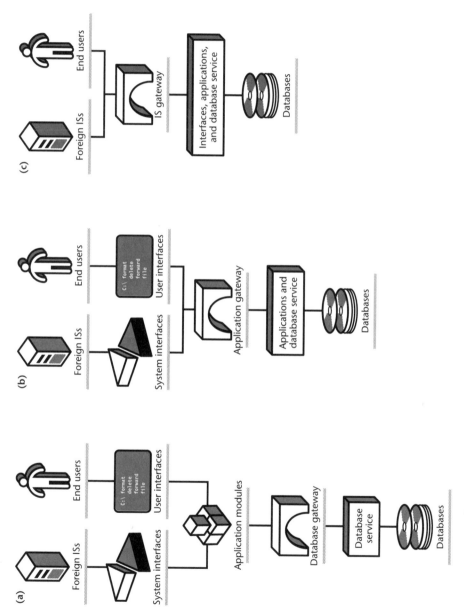

FIGURE 1.6 Gateway types and placements in IS architectures. For simplicity, target ISs are not shown. (a) The database gateway used with decomposable legacy ISs. (b) The application gateway used with semidecomposable legacy ISs. (c) The IS gateway used with nondecomposable legacy ISs.

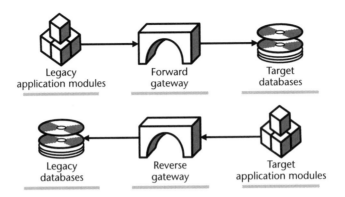

FIGURE 1.7 Forward and reverse gateways.

interfaces can have a significant, negative effect on the viability of the content and performance of an IS, as well as all the ISs and people that interact with it. Interface migration is crucial to the success of the entire legacy migration, and therefore it must be given much consideration.

User interfaces significantly affect the working environment and productivity of a large number of people. Imagine if, for example, you ran a bank and your tellers were unable to access the database to enter transactions. Consider the consequences of the loss of time and customer confidence. The system interfaces significantly influence the efficiency of all current and future ISs that interact with the target IS. If the system can't access the IS, it can't perform its function. Interfaces are critical before, during, and after the legacy IS migration. Indeed, the success of the migration depends critically on the interfaces to the composite IS.

> The IS gateway is crucial to the success of the interface migration, which, in turn, is crucial to the success of the entire IS migration.

Interface migration should be considered equally with database and applications migration. This makes sense technically, since interfaces, databases, and applications have distinct technical challenges and supporting technologies. The separation of interface, database, and application issues and technologies is part of a trend toward next-generation IS technologies, architectures, and methods. The idea is to separate as many aspects as possible to achieve, among other goals, greater modularity, flexibility, reusability, and portability. This is widely discussed in terms of enterprise information architectures and middleware. More information about this can be found in Brodie's article (Brodie 1992).

Interface migration can be used to implement corporate-wide interface improvements (e.g., TTY to GUI) and standardization. These improvements are currently being pursued in most IS organizations. Interface migration can provide a basis for, and many of the benefits of, IS integration and interoperability before they are provided at the database and application levels.

Although putting a new interface on a legacy IS involves significant work, it is not as technically challenging as building database gateways or scrubbers, or decomposing and selectively migrating legacy applications. There are many tools for building user interfaces, some very powerful indeed. Hence, a new interface can be built that can translate requests made on the new user interface into calls against the underlying legacy and target applications. This gives the appearance to users of integration and may even provide some actual IS integration. For example, the new user interface could translate a single request (e.g., menu selection, icon click) into calls to two or more legacy or target ISs, thus achieving a degree of interoperability, even if those underlying ISs do not interoperate other than through the new user interface.

During migration, legacy IS modules and their interfaces can operate simultaneously with the corresponding target IS modules and their interfaces. This may require that the desktop machine (PC or workstation) of the target environment emulate a *dumb terminal* interface. For IBM legacy code, the PC must include 3270 emulation, a widely available feature. As a result, the user interface could get ugly during the migration with GUI windows existing simultaneously with 3270 windows on the PC. These problems can be addressed by an IS gateway, specifically by the features developed especially for user interface migration. The user interface migration component offers a single user interface that can help to simplify the multiple interfaces of the composite IS. It can also hide the fact that the functions are being supported by the legacy IS, the new IS, or both. This helps to insulate IS users from changes in the user interface as well as IS changes.

The user interface migration component of the IS gateway is a key to successful interface migration. It insulates all end users and interfacing systems from potential negative effects of the migration, as illustrated in Figure 1.8. An IS gateway captures user and system interface calls to some applications and then translates and redirects them to other applications or application interfaces. It also accepts the corresponding application responses and translates, integrates, and redirects them to the calling interface. For some legacy interfaces, this means capturing TTY keystrokes (called screen scraping) and mapping them into GUI interfaces or directly to applications. An IS gateway provides more independence between the interfaces and the applications, thus adding to the flexibility of the corresponding migration methods. Besides gateway functionality, it could provide a complete user interface development and management environment. It might also support migration with versioning and other functionality. Finally, the IS gateway can be maintained as part of the target IS architecture to support future interface migration and evolution.

A large insurance company we know tried to upgrade 2,500 workstations in their East Coast service center over a two-week period. This led to considerable confusion and bad feelings by staff. This migration did work, but there was no comprehensive plan to migrate to a target user interface with which agents could access all necessary ISs, legacy or new. The migration was to new workstations that would process GUIs and support local processing. The new GUIs were evolutionary as opposed to revolutionary advances. Once installed, management saw that the GUIs should be more IS-independent, and a subsequent target user interface environment design was launched and is underway.

We hope they develop a smooth migration or evolution plan so that Agnes, who has been an agent for them for 15 years, doesn't sabotage the system. We visited such a service center and talked to agents who had found many ways to sabotage the new user interfaces. One major point of sabotage was to trick the new systems into providing more favorable statistics on customer contact times.

The user interface migration component of the IS gateway permits the changes to be phased in at a rate appropriate to the user community. IS gateways can also be used to introduce, temporarily, functionality and extensions intended for the target IS. These can be added earlier to gain some benefits—for example, essential edit checks not in the legacy interfaces and not yet available in the target interfaces. This adds alternatives, hence flexibility, to the migration method.

One large, nationwide corporation had (before downsizing and reengineering) 12 service centers across the United States. Each center housed a large number of agents (e.g., 50 to a shift) using the legacy IS interfaces to conduct their jobs. It was infeasible to imagine that approximately 800 user interfaces and old workstations could be replaced overnight with new interfaces and the necessary new workstations. What was considered more reasonable was that one service center would be incrementally migrated (i.e., a few workstations and agents in a pilot study, then others) to the migration environment. After a successful migration, then the other service centers would be migrated on the basis of their local conditions (e.g., training, budget, workload). The corporate downsizing plan was to merge the 12 service centers into four and subsequently into fewer. So only those service centers that would remain were migrated. The others were left untouched until they were closed, some four months down the road.

Note that the above migration was to a "migration environment" and not to the target user interfaces. That would have been too large a step. This rollout was planned in a reasonable way, or so the company thought. However, they discovered a problem with the first increment of the user interface migration. They lost agent support by failing to consider the agents in the process. The first increment in the user interface migration was considered by most agents as very threatening. They much preferred their ugly old green-and-black IBM 3270s to the fancy GUIs provided on the new workstation.

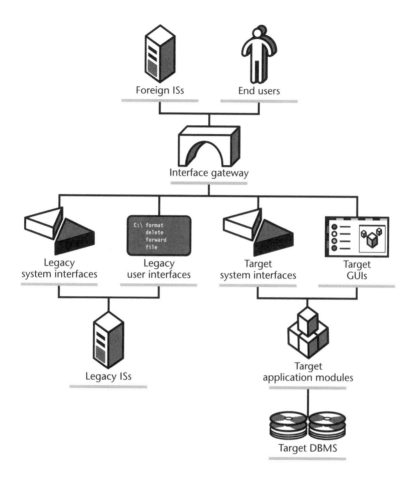

FIGURE 1.8 IS gateway.

Indeed, the fancy GUIs made them feel insecure and controlled by the big boys in the head office. Once management realized their oversight in employee relations, it was decided to involve the agents in the process. They were given training and the opportunity to suggest what they'd like in the GUIs. So, through this incremental user interface migration, a significant problem was detected and corrected before the remaining 850 user interfaces/workstations were migrated, nationwide.

Because of the significance of human interfaces with information systems, as well as the trends toward better interfaces and more powerful graphics, an increasing emphasis is being placed on the design, development, and evolution of user interfaces. Indeed, the increased focus on quality and customer support has led to the need for agents who use the user interfaces to ISs to be able to access, via their user interface, as many ISs as may be necessary during an interaction with a customer. This leads to the need for interoperability between ISs. That is, the agent must be able to access or interoperate, through the same user interface, with multiple ISs. In turn, this means that the user interface to be provided is unlikely to be IS-specific as it was with legacy ISs. The user interface must be designed independently of the ISs that are or might be included in the agent's current or future function. So user interface design and evolution from legacy user interfaces (e.g., merging of previously IS-specific user interfaces) is a significant design issue. Indeed, it is a matter of research. See, for example, the article "Reengineering User Interfaces" in *IEEE Software* (IEEE 1995b).

1.9 PREPARATION AND GLOBAL DESIGN

In all significant, large-scale legacy IS migrations, the challenges and consequent resource requirements will be immense. The migration may involve problems, such as database integration, scrubbing, and translation, that have no practical solution other than vast manual effort by experts in the technology and application domain. Hence, every effort should be made to radically reduce the scope of the problem.

> We argue against global anything and for incremental everything.

You should first consider radically reducing the functions and data that will be necessary for the target information system. Much legacy data and many functions may be entirely unnecessary to support current or future business requirements. Since the migration challenge is, in our estimate, exponential to the size of the legacy to be migrated, much is to be saved and risk diminished by judicious reduction of noncritical data and function.

In other words, avoid migration wherever possible. In keeping with the spirit of reengineering, radically simplify your information systems. Learn to get along with less. This practice should become habit throughout the migration. Radical reduction of functions and data is not only the initial design step for the entire migration process: It should be applied at the beginning of every incremental step.

We now outline the global design of the target IS. We do not dwell on this, since we argue against global anything and for incremental everything. Global design, to the extent it is required, should be done as if you have a clean sheet of paper or a green field. These wonderful and impractical metaphors mean that you should design as if working with no constraints. However, because of the nature of the legacy IS migration and our assumptions to minimize risk and reimplement legacy functionality, you must constrain your global and incremental designs by the extent to which legacy anything is to be included in the target. This should be balanced by design methods and principles that would diminish these constraints in the target IS. Take steps to avoid the problems of the legacy IS with your design.

Let us emphasize this point further. For significant-sized legacy ISs, the migration will take many years. Hence, it is impossible to do a detailed design that will remain valid throughout the migration. So a detailed global design is a waste of effort and a hindrance to the entire project. More generally, given the scale of the legacy IS of interest, comprehensive anything is an impossible first step. Everything must be done incrementally, including the design. Just as the Cold Turkey migration is infeasible, so are global schema and function designs. How do you know if a design works until you test it out practically?

On the other hand, you can't build a castle brick by brick without a total design in mind. Therefore, do as much global design as necessary and incrementally fill out the details on demand in subsequent incremental steps. You will also have to modify the global design as requirements change through changing business requirements and technical corrections.

Radical simplification is one of the themes of reengineering. The less data you collect, the less you will need to manage and process. Consider this story from a large manufacturing plant. Their legacy business process for part costing was as follows. Since labor dominated the cost of parts, the company managed the labor invested in each part. As raw materials entered the manufacturing line, each material had a card associated with it. As the raw materials arrived at each station, the employee entered on the card the start work time, the type of action performed, and then the completion time when it left the station. To this information was added, via an IS, the labor rate of the employee. This continued through 20 or more stations until the part was completed. The cost of the part was computed as a complex formula involving this and other data, all of which was archived. A multiplicative factor was applied, depending on the raw materials used (e.g., 180% for cadmium alloy products). Just imagine the amount of data, the number of errors, and the points of sabotage in this process.

The reengineered process works this way. On Monday, or whenever, the manufacturing line is fired up. The costs of running the line are accumulated, including raw materials, total labor time for employees on the line, and so on. When the line is shut down, say on Friday, the cost per part is calculated by dividing the total cost by the number of completed parts. In this case, the legacy IS is irrelevant to the new business process and need not—indeed, should not—be migrated. Toss it and all the code!

The global, and incomplete, design is to be used to guide the migration. For all design steps, do not complete a comprehensive design of the target. Rather, develop a high-level design for the scope of the migration domain. On demand, create a detailed design of the increment to be migrated.

In addition to the aforementioned radical reduction step, a second global design step is the development of a global design of the target information system, following our above advice. This includes the interfaces, functions, and data. Consider global schema design. You may need to design a global schema down to the level of repositories (e.g., data servers, general contents) or down to the level of entities and some relationships. You will not likely need precise designs except for the increment to be migrated. Design should be done on demand. The same could be said of applications or individual functions.

> ### MIGRATION GROUNDWORK
>
> - Radically reduce functions and data.
> - Develop a global design of the target IS.
> - Design the target environment.
> - Design the migration framework.

A third initial design step is the design of the target environment, following our above advice that comprehensive anything is impossible. Advances in core technology (e.g., hardware, communications, operating systems, data management, programming languages) as well as constantly changing business requirements argue that you should design the target environment to be as flexible as possible. In the case of the environment, this is referred to as *portability*. However, considering migration to future requirements, portability can be seen in a more comprehensive light under which anything can be changed without significant negative impact. For example, do not bind the target IS to a specific operating system, database management system, or programming language. As with global schema and function designs, develop a global design of the target environment and provide a detailed design only as required for incremental steps.

A fourth initial design step is the design of the migration framework. The migration framework includes the legacy IS, the target IS, and the composite IS, which includes the legacy, the target, and the intermediate components such as the gateways. As with any IS, the migration framework has several aspects: the environment, the interfaces, the functions, and the data. Specifically, the migration framework includes the mapping between the source objects and their target counterparts. Following the vital incremental nature of the migration, complete a global design of the framework and provide details, on demand, for each incremental step.

1.10 THE CHICKEN LITTLE STEPS

Migration requirements vary from legacy IS to legacy IS. As we've already established, the legacy architecture plays a role in determining the complexity of the migration. The operational context of the legacy is also a factor. By operational context, we mean the technical and business needs that the legacy IS supports. These needs are unique to each organization, and they can significantly reduce or increase the number of migration requirements. To make matters more difficult, the legacy migration requirements and the business/technical migration requirements frequently conflict. Examples of migration requirements for a typical legacy include the following:

- Migrate in place.

- Ensure continuous, safe, reliable, robust, ready access to mission-critical functions and information at performance levels adequate to support the business workload.

- Make as many fixes, improvements, and enhancements as reasonable to address current and anticipated requirements.

- Make as few changes as possible to reduce migration complexity and risk.

- Alter the legacy code as little as possible to minimize risk.

- Alter the legacy code to facilitate migration.

- Establish as much flexibility as possible to facilitate future evolution.

- Minimize the potential negative impacts of change, including those on users, applications, databases, and, particularly, on the on-going operation of the mission-critical IS.

- Maximize the benefits of modern technology and methods.

Our migration method is tailorable to address such requirements. You can adapt Chicken Little to fit the unique requirements of your legacy IS.

The Chicken Little migration method consists of a number of individual migration elements that together achieve the desired migration. Each element handles a specific aspect of the migration, such as migrating the database, migrating an application, or installing the target environment. We've elected to call these migration components *steps*.

The greater the independence of the steps, the greater the flexibility for adapting a migration method to specific migration requirements, changing requirements, and mistakes. Independent steps can proceed independently in any order. Gateways are one of the primary means of providing independence between steps, since they can encapsulate system components that are undergoing change behind an unchanging interface. We want to stress here that the steps do not necessarily have to proceed in sequence. The unique requirements of your legacy IS might demand otherwise. Depending on the characteristics of your legacy environment, the order of the steps might change, or certain steps might be combined into one. Furthermore, several steps might be in progress at one time. The steps are meant to be flexible and tailorable to individual needs.

> Independent steps can proceed independently in any order.

31

The Chicken Little Steps

1. Incrementally analyze the legacy IS.
2. Incrementally decompose the legacy IS structure.
3. Incrementally design the target interfaces.
4. Incrementally design the target applications.
5. Incrementally design the target database.
6. Incrementally install the target environment.
7. Incrementally create and install the necessary gateways.
8. Incrementally migrate the legacy database.
9. Incrementally migrate the legacy applications.
10. Incrementally migrate the legacy interfaces.
11. Incrementally cut over to the target IS.

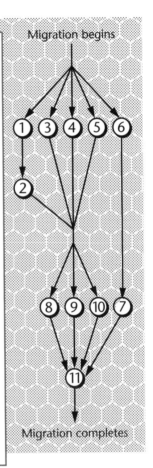

Ideally, to permit work to proceed in parallel, the steps of the method should be as independent as possible. The chart above indicates how the steps can proceed. You can start with analyzing the legacy IS (step 1), designing the target IS (any of steps 3, 4, or 5), or installing the target environment (step 6). You can decompose the legacy IS (step 2) after you've completed step 1. To install the gateway (step 7), you must have already installed the target environment (step 6). You can migrate the interfaces, applications, or database (steps 8, 9, 10), or install the gateway (step 7), in any order. When you have completed those steps, you are ready to cut over the IS (step 11). The above description is not for the entire IS, since that would be a Cold Turkey migration. The above flow of steps is for each increment to be migrated, so the entire flow is repeated for each increment.

It should be noted that some steps need not be done for each increment. If, for step 7, you use a general-purpose or purchased gateway that is useful for many steps, then you can skip step 7 for most of the increments and go directly from steps 2, 3, 4, 5, and 6 to 8, 9, or 10. Similarly, if the increment is of adequate size—for example, step 6, installing the target environment—it can be skipped entirely until another increment is required to support other increments. For example, you may install a minimal environment on which to prototype all migration steps before installing the stuff further in the company. In this case, step 6 can be skipped until you are ready to move out of the prototype.

A significant challenge for most migrations is to plan, manage, and modify, as needed, the steps and their interactions. A related challenge is to create a migration plan that is adequately coordinated to achieve incremental and parallel migration steps. The steps discussed in this book are intended to provide this flexibility so that they can be tailored to the requirements and available resources.

One of the goals of legacy systems migration (and, for that matter, nearly every process in the IS world) is risk reduction and management. The incremental nature of the Chicken Little strategy leads to two ways to reduce risk. First, there must always be a fail-safe fallback position, should any incremental step fail. Second, the increment size must be chosen to make the risk of the current step acceptably small (e.g., zero). *We offer no new ways of evaluating such risks, but we do emphasize the importance of risk evaluation, control, management, and avoidance.*

Here we briefly discuss each of the above steps in the general context of Chicken Little migration. In the subsequent chapters we explore the steps in more detail and in a situational context. We consider Chicken Little migration from various types of legacy environments.

Step 1: Incrementally Analyze the Legacy IS

It is imperative that you understand your legacy IS in appropriate detail. Learn as much about it as you need. You'll have some gaps to fill since, as we discussed earlier, the requirements for the legacy environment are likely to be nonexistent or, at best, hopelessly out-of-date. Really what you'll be doing is developing requirements for the legacy IS and for the target IS. In effect, the legacy IS is reverse-engineered back to the requirements phase. Make sure that you make progress toward specific information requirements established by a need to know. Without focus, you can fall into analysis paralysis.

Step 2: Incrementally Decompose the Legacy IS Structure

The charter in this step includes modifying the legacy IS to ensure that it is decomposable. Dependencies between modules, such as procedure calls, must be removed. There must be well-defined interfaces between the modules and the database services.

The cost of this step depends on the current structure of the legacy IS. If such a restructuring is not possible, other variations of this migration method (discussed later in the book) might need to be investigated.

Step 3: Incrementally Design the Target Interfaces

Design and specify the user interfaces (typically GUIs) and system interfaces of the target IS. Your interface migration strategy should be planned at this stage, including the decision of whether an IS gateway should be built. The target modules and interfaces will run on the client machines in the target environment. If significant functionality is not being added during the migration, legacy and target application module functions should be intentionally similar to one another.

Step 4: Incrementally Design the Target Applications

The applications that will run on the target platforms must be designed in accordance with the business rules and processes that will be supported in the target environment. Whether those applications will be reengineered from those of the legacy environment or will closely match the legacy applications in terms of functionality and process flow is up to you. Your decision should be made on the basis of the analysis and risk assessment of your Chicken Little migration.

Step 5: Incrementally Design the Target Database

Design a relational schema to meet the data requirements of the target IS. Unless there are very unusual requirements, we recommend the use of an SQL-based, relational DBMS. This requires an understanding of the target and legacy ISs and uses the results of the previous steps. Depending on the legacy code and the application requirements, the target database design step can be very complex. Legacy IS development techniques can make data definitions and structures difficult to find and understand. Before the age of databases, the distinction between data and application code was often blurred. It was also common to distribute data definitions throughout the application. There is currently a trend back to these ideas. Object-oriented and distributed computing principles suggest moving from a single, centralized database schema to distributed class definitions that encapsulate data and functions. The use of an advanced technology such as object orientation must be weighed in terms of risk, requirements, and reward.

Step 6: Incrementally Install the Target Environment

Identify the requirements for the target environment on the basis of the total target IS requirements. In effect, treat the target environment as if it were being developed from scratch exclusive of the migration-oriented issues.

Next, select the environment and test it in a rudimentary check-out of performance and other characteristics. Then install the target environment, preferably featuring a desktop computer for each target IS user (bank clerk, telephone service order clerk, etc.) and appropriate server machines. This requires replacing a dumb terminal with a PC or workstation and connecting them with a local area network. Such a move to desktop, client/server computing is currently being studied in most IS shops and is being implemented in many. This facilitates the construction of GUI programs and off-loading code from a server machine, where MIPS are typically expensive, to a client machine, where MIPS are essentially free.

Step 7: Incrementally Create and Install the Necessary Gateways

Develop your gateway requirements on the basis of your application requirements. Consider function, architectural placement, and non-functional requirements (e.g., platform, OS, performance). It's likely that several gateways will be needed. Then make the build versus buy decision. Chapter 10 will help you. Once you've built or bought your gateways, install them.

Step 8: Incrementally Migrate the Legacy Database

Install the target DBMS on the server machines, implementing the schema resulting from step 5 (the design of the target database). Migrate the legacy database to the target DBMS under the new schema, and use the gateway to support the legacy application calls. You will have to download, scrub, convert, and upload (usually) large amounts of data.

Note that this step can be incremental. Portions of data can be moved at a time. This complicates the gateway function.

Step 9: Incrementally Migrate the Legacy Applications

Select and migrate legacy modules, one (or more) at a time. Selection should be based on technical and organizational criteria. What is simplest? What are the cost considerations? What is needed most? This step involves rewriting the legacy modules to run directly against the modern DBMS.

Step 10: Incrementally Migrate the Legacy Interfaces

Select and migrate legacy interfaces, one (or more) at a time. If a 4GL is used that supports application and interface development, interface and application migration might be coordinated. In this case, the legacy user and system interfaces must be rewritten to run directly against the modern DBMS. The target interfaces will run on a client machine in a 4GL/GUI environment on the desktop. They can be used to replace the legacy interfaces that run on dumb terminals. Meanwhile, the remaining legacy interfaces must continue to be used. An IS gateway could be used here to support interface migration.

Step 11: Incrementally Cut Over to the Target IS

Cutover, discussed in Section 1.11, is the process of switching from a legacy IS to the corresponding target IS component. Operations from the legacy are cut over to the target IS in increments according to specific requirements. Accompanying the cutover are configuration management and version control issues, as discussed in Section 1.12.

1.11 CUTOVER

A key problem in Cold Turkey migrations is that cutover is unmanageable and exposes the organization to the risks of the as-yet nonoperational target system. As with all other aspects of migration, a Chicken Little cutover must be incremental and dealt with in its own right. In this section we discuss that process.

We use the term *cutover* to refer to the process of switching operations or access from a legacy IS component to the corresponding target IS component. Whereas the application migration step is used to design, build, and install target applications, the cutover step is used to incrementally cut over operations from the legacy applications to the target applications, application by application, site by site, and user by user according to specific requirements.

> Cutover, like all the Chicken Little steps, can be tailored to suit your unique needs. It can be incremental, and it can also proceed with the remaining steps in parallel.

Although there could be a cutover phase as a component of any of the steps of the migration process, the size and complexity of the ISs we are considering can warrant a separate cutover step. In large organizations, such as banks and telecommunications companies, IS cutover may involve hundreds of sites, hundreds of users, and hundreds of versions of legacy and target database, application, and interface modules. Target modules may be ready months or years before the target environment is in place or before all end users are prepared for the change. The cutover step involves coordinating all these components so that the composite IS continues to meet the mission-critical daily operational IS requirements. This complexity alone can warrant a separate cutover step.

The size of the cutover step may require that it be incremental—performed in appropriately sized chunks—and thus consistent with the Chicken Little strategy. It can also be optimal to proceed with all steps in parallel. For example, some hardware and software in certain sites can be cut over for users while the corresponding legacy components are still in operation. Incremental and parallel cutover increases the flexibility of the method but also increases the complexity of the cutover procedure, further motivating cutover as a separate step. Every situation has the potential to be different from any other; therefore, every situation must be evaluated accordingly.

1.12 VERSION CONTROL AND CONFIGURATION MANAGEMENT

Complicating the migration process—in particular, the cutover step—is the need for enhanced version control and configuration management of both legacy and target environment components. Whether applications code, user interface modules, gateway interfaces, databases and repositories, or other components of the IS environment as a whole, these tasks are more complex than they are with "simple" systems development because of the composite nature of the migration process.

As the operational version of the information system evolves from its legacy state to its eventual form in the target environment, the configuration management realm will likewise shade from legacy-intensive to, over time, one with more of its responsibilities in the target system. During this process, however, these issues must be addressed:

> Constant change in business requirements and technology advances will force all future ISs to be migrated constantly.

- multiple-platform version control of code

- supporting documentation for the composite IS

All code—in applications, data definition language (DDL), data manipulation language (DML), user interface modules, and so on—must be considered. By supporting documentation, we mean in-line documentation as well as that applicable to the user community. As time goes on and the migration progresses, for example, the user interface will likely shift from terminal-oriented to GUI. But this is not likely for all applications at the same time. Therefore, the various versions and configurations of the documentation related to the users must likewise incrementally shift.

Repository technology is being developed by many vendors to address such requirements. Some early products with partial functionality are already available. Because of the complexity of future distributed-computing environments and systems, such repositories will become increasingly critical. The properties we see in the legacy IS migrations will become commonplace to all ISs. That is, constant change in business requirements and technology advances, will force all future information systems to be migrated constantly. Evolution will be a dominant requirement of all future ISs.

1.13 PREVENTING NEW LEGACY ISs

Today's new system is tomorrow's legacy. Unfortunately, we will never be able to prevent legacy information systems. We can use the best tools and methods to reduce their resistance to necessary change, and we can build them in modules that allow and even facilitate change. But we cannot anticipate future business requirements or advances in technology. Both of these may pose challenges to our information systems that we cannot now see, hence raising the future resistance of our information systems to these changes.

A wise choice of target environment and architecture will facilitate later developments, such as porting the application as required to a wide variety of current and future desktop machines and deploying the database on various computing platforms. As needed, the target IS can readily be ported to environments appropriate to current and future requirements. That is, the target IS is designed to be very flexible—portable—to aid current and future rightsizing and to reduce the possibility of becoming a future legacy IS, complete with all of the associated problems of a legacy IS.

It may be surprising to note that with many large legacy IS migration efforts, subsequent transition of already-completed portions is required long before the initial migration program is complete. Large legacy IS migrations may easily take five to eight years. During the course of such a prolonged effort, organizational planners will no doubt wish to take advantage of new technologies that have evolved since the completion of early migration steps.

Consider the Internal Revenue Service's tax modernization system (TMS) effort, currently underway in the U.S. Department of Treasury. This program is expected to continue past the year 2000. Given the frequent changes in tax laws and other attributes of the internal revenue collection process, individual target-migration components will likely undergo subsequent transition before the overall program is completed. Just as there are incremental changes to business requirements (e.g., individual tax laws as opposed to the entire tax code), so should there be methods to support incremental changes to TMS. The migration methods presented in this book are based on the observation that incremental change is natural and necessary.

1.14 CLOSING REMARKS

In Chapter 1, we set the stage for the discussions and case studies of the subsequent chapters. We discussed the characteristics of a legacy IS in detail. We also examined the primary shortcomings of a legacy IS—the ones that keep your business from remaining competitive. Its high-cost maintenance monopolizes the time of your technical personnel and drains your budget, precluding investment in modern technologies, tools, and models. Moreover, the legacy IS resists change. It cannot evolve as your business needs evolve. If your IS can't support your current business needs, your company loses its competitive edge.

The commonsense solution to the legacy IS problem is migration. We talked about the Cold Turkey migration strategy and discussed its limitations. Then we introduced our incremental migration method, Chicken Little, which is the focus of this book. Chicken Little permits you to control risk by migrating in increments of your own choosing. The use of gateways is an essential factor in the success of Chicken Little migration. We spent some time elaborating on the ways that gateways can smooth the migration process.

We also established the parameters of the migration models that we analyze in later chapters. We focused on the different types of architecture an IS might have—decomposable, semidecomposable, nondecomposable, or a hybrid of all these. As we discuss in subsequent chapters, the Chicken Little migration steps vary depending on the architectural constructs and requirements of a given legacy environment.

Bear in mind that business reengineering can take place in conjunction with the technology-oriented migration. As new IS components are introduced, new ways of doing business may be incorporated into the organization, all with an eye toward future flexibility.

Chapter 2

MIGRATING DECOMPOSABLE LEGACY ISs

*C*hapter 2 describes our incremental migration methodology, known as Chicken Little, and applies it to decomposable legacy IS migration. As we noted in the first chapter, the Chicken Little methodology is tailorable to legacy environments ranging from the most challenging—aging mainframe-based applications with numerous undesirable attributes—to those that might be termed legacy systems in the making. These are systems that will possess many undesirable characteristics of legacy IS environments a few years down the road, although the problem hasn't grown to crisis proportions at this time.

What works for the worst cases can be modified for less risky ones. For the worst case we assume the greatest risk of failure. The methodology hinges on the size of the increments chosen for the migration steps. The guidelines are simple: the smaller the increment, the less risky the migration step, should it fail.

There is a trade-off with respect to the size of the migration increment, however. The smaller the increment, the more complex the gateway must be. Further, areas like version control and configuration management are also more complex and risky.

Many ISs are smaller than those discussed in the case studies in Chapters 3 and 5. Hence the methodology for them can be modified *accordingly. Also, management may wish to take on greater risk, hoping to achieve greater rewards. The rewards include a shorter span of time until new technology is deployed and a higher payback on the investment in new technology.*

Chicken Little permits you to choose the level of risk. You can change the degree of risk with each step, since larger or smaller increments can be chosen. Risk can be increased by making larger increments in successive steps and increasing the number and complexity of parallel steps, and by shortening the time period to complete the individual steps or the entire migration effort.

Chicken Little must be tailored to the characteristics of your individual organization. Contributing factors such as budgets, skills, and strategic corporate direction will dictate the form that any given migration program using our methodology will take. The investment-risk-reward equation common to most areas of IS technology and business as a whole characterizes the tailoring and implementation of Chicken Little.

2.1 DECOMPOSABLE ARCHITECTURES AND CHICKEN LITTLE

In Chapter 1, we discussed three architectural classes of legacy ISs: decomposable, semidecomposable, and nondecomposable. Decomposable ISs are the most modular of the three, with demarcations among the system interfaces, user interfaces, application modules, and database service. Compartmentalized migration is easier for decomposable ISs. The more complex requirements and architectures of semidecomposable and nondecomposable ISs are successively harder to migrate.

The goal of the migration process is a target IS that is itself decomposable and is in our target environment (e.g., rightsized computers, client/server architecture, modern software, etc.). Decomposability in the target IS is intended to facilitate future change, thus avoiding future legacy IS problems.

In this chapter, we discuss three methods for migration of decomposable legacy ISs. Each method has 11 components, or steps, that have been tailored to fit the requirements of a decomposable IS. These methods are

- forward migration

- reverse migration

- general migration (a combination of forward and reverse migration)

A forward migration involves an initial migration of the entire database environment, followed by the installation of a forward database gateway. Using the forward database gateway, the legacy applications can access the post-migration data management environment. Subsequently, the applications are transitioned in tailorable Chicken Little increments.

Conversely, the reverse migration postpones the database migration until the end of the process. The target applications are created and installed on a reverse gateway that permits access to the legacy database. Then they are tested and made ready to run. When the target environment is complete, the legacy database is migrated. The reverse gateway can be removed, since the target applications can run directly against the target database.

The general migration method involves a combination of both forward and reverse migration steps, subject to the characteristics of the applications and the databases. The gateway is more complex than the gateways of the forward and reverse methods. It contains the functions of forward gateway, reverse gateway, mapping table, and coordinator.

On their own, the forward and reverse migrations are not typically applicable to many legacy ISs. Databases are often too large for the Cold Turkey migrations required at the beginning of the forward migration and at the end of the reverse migration. For example, this is the case if the time to download the legacy database, scrub it, and transform it into the target is longer than the IS can afford to be down in terms of not supporting its business requirements. Large databases for even medium-size organizations can take days or weeks to download, without even considering the processing necessary to scrub and reformat.

> Forward and reverse migration principles are applied in all subsequent migration methods.

Both forward and reverse methods used together are necessary for an incremental database migration. Throughout the migration, some database increments have been migrated to the target database, while some will remain in the legacy databases of files. The forward gateway provides legacy applications access to the target database while the reverse gateway permits access by target applications to legacy data. Hence, we must understand both methods on their own as well as in concert in the general migration method.

We discuss each of these methods in turn. In combination, the descriptions will introduce you to the Chicken Little incremental approach. Specifically, the descriptions of the forward and reverse migration methods will provide you with a basis of understanding that is fundamental to an understanding of the general decomposable migration method.

2.2 FORWARD MIGRATION METHOD

The forward migration method requires the database to be migrated in one initial, Cold Turkey step. It involves a forward database gateway. This gateway aids Chicken Little migration of the applications and their interfaces *after* the Cold Turkey database migration. The approach is called a forward migration because it migrates unchanged legacy applications *forward* onto a modern DBMS and then migrates the legacy applications to new target applications. The requirement for Cold Turkey database migration at the beginning of the process, as well as other limitations, are likely to make this approach inappropriate for most situations.

> A forward migration migrates unchanged legacy applications forward onto a modern DBMS and then migrates the legacy application to new target applications.

The forward migration method is an 11-step process. These specially tailored steps are as follows. As in Chapter 1, the flowchart indicates how the steps can proceed. You can start with analyzing the legacy IS (step 1), designing the target IS (any of steps 3, 4, or 5), or installing the target environment (step 6). You can decompose the legacy IS (step 2) after you've completed step 1. To install the forward database gateway

The Chicken Little Steps

1. Incrementally analyze the legacy IS.
2. Incrementally decompose the legacy IS structure.
3. Incrementally design the target interfaces.
4. Incrementally design the target applications.
5. Incrementally design the target database.
6. Incrementally install the target environment.
7. Incrementally create and install the forward database gateway.
8. Migrate the legacy database.
9. Incrementally migrate the legacy applications.
10. Incrementally migrate the legacy interfaces.
11. Incrementally cut over to the target IS.

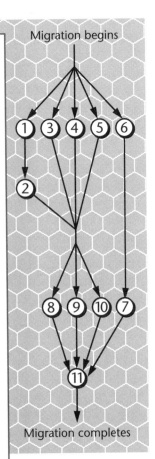

(step 7), you must have already installed the target environment (step 6). You can migrate the interfaces, applications, or database (steps 8, 9, 10), or install the forward database gateway (step 7), in any order. When you have completed those steps, you are ready to cut over the IS (step 11). The above description is not for the entire IS, since that would be a Cold Turkey migration. The above flow of steps is for each increment to be migrated, so the entire flow is repeated for each such increment.

As you can see, steps 7 and 8 have been tailored to fit the requirements for forward migration of a decomposable legacy IS. To show how the migration works, let's look at all of the steps in detail.

Step 1: Incrementally Analyze the Legacy IS

It is imperative to understand the legacy IS to the degree necessary for the migration. Because of the successive increase in complexity and in risk of failure, each migration increment must be understood in appropriate detail. This corresponds to developing requirements for the legacy IS and for the target IS. As we discussed in Chapter 1, the requirements for the legacy environment are likely either no longer in existence or, at best, hopelessly out-of-date. In effect, the legacy IS is reverse-engineered back to the requirements phase.

Sources for understanding include documentation, if any exists; the code; and the people who support, manage, and use the legacy IS. Existing tools can assist with this step, for example, KnowledgeWare's Legacy Workbench and Bachman Information Systems' Analyst are useful for code analysis. Remember to include new target IS requirements in your analysis. Otherwise, you won't be prepared for the increasing complexity of the migration, and the success of your project will be at greater risk.

The techniques needed to acquire this legacy IS understanding involve modeling of existing applications, such as entity-relationship modeling for the data management component, data flow diagramming for the application processes, or any other appropriate modeling technique. As CASE environments with repository-based finely granular object interrelationships and inter-tool notification servers become more of a reality, such environments will make legacy IS analysis easier.

Step 2: Incrementally Decompose the Legacy IS Structure

The charter in this step requires modifying the legacy IS to ensure that it is decomposable. Dependencies between modules, such as procedure calls, must be removed. There must be well-defined interfaces between the modules and the database services.

While at first it might seem curious to modify applications in a legacy environment that are merely going to be transitioned to the target environment, the philosophy is much the same as fixing the dents and paint scrapes on your car before you trade it in or put it up for sale. A bit of time and money invested up front can help you sell your car or, in the case of legacy IS migration, ease the process under which the phased transition will occur.

The cost of this step depends on the current structure of the code and the legacy IS. Some code, regardless of age, technology, and so on, may or may not be decomposable. However, decomposing ISs or restructuring them is a very difficult procedure and may easily weaken systems. There are a range of tools to assist with such modifications. These are generally intended for improving structure so as to prolong the life of an IS. If such a restructuring is not possible, other Chicken Little migration methods discussed later in the book might need to be investigated.

Step 3: Incrementally Design the Target Interfaces

Designing and specifying the target interfaces first requires designing the software architecture of the target IS, illustrated in Figure 2.1. The design should include a modern DBMS and target database that might be centralized, on one server machine or distributed over the multiple servers in a client/server or distributed DBMS architecture. It also should include the corresponding user interfaces and system interfaces.

The target GUIs, system interfaces, and an interface migration strategy should be planned, including the decision of whether an IS gateway should be built. An IS gateway is almost always recommended, at least to deal with the user interface migration. The target modules and interfaces will run on the client machines in the target environment. If significant functionality is not being added during the migration, legacy and target application module functions should be intentionally similar.

Step 4: Incrementally Design the Target Applications

In a process similar to that used for the target interfaces in step 3, design and specify the target applications. The applications that will run on the target platforms must be designed in accordance with the business processes and rules that will be supported by the target environment. Whether those applications will be reengineered from those of the legacy environment or will closely match the legacy applications in terms of functionality and process flow is one of the

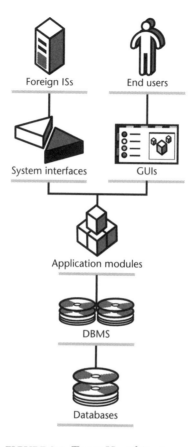

FIGURE 2.1 Target IS architecture.

decisions that must be made with respect to the analysis and risk assessment of the Chicken Little migration.

Step 5: Incrementally Design the Target Database

The next step is to design a relational database schema to meet the data requirements of the target IS. Unless there are very unusual requirements, we recommend the use of an SQL-based, relational DBMS. In any case, a conventional DBMS evaluation should be conducted, as with any new information system. This requires an understanding of the target and legacy ISs and uses the results of the previous steps. Depending on the legacy code and the application requirements, the target database design step can be very complex.

Legacy IS development techniques can make data definitions and structures difficult to find and understand. Before the age of databases, the distinction between data and application code was often blurred. It was also common to distribute data definitions throughout the application. There is currently a trend back to these ideas. Object-oriented and distributed computing principles suggest moving from a single, centralized database schema to distributed class definitions that encapsulate data and functions.

The complexity of this step can be large enough to warrant migrating in small increments, as discussed in Section 2.3. Reengineering tools, such as Bachman Information Systems' Re-Engineering Product Set, can be used to extract data definitions from legacy code, to design schema fragments for each increment, and to integrate the schema fragment into a single schema.

Step 6: Incrementally Install the Target Environment

The process begins with identifying the requirements for the target environment on the basis of the total target IS requirements. In effect, treat the target environment as if it were being developed from scratch, exclusive of the migration-oriented issues.

Once the environment is selected, test it and tune its performance. Then the target environment, typically consisting of a desktop computer for each target IS user (for example, a bank clerk or a telephone service order clerk) and appropriate server machines, should be installed. This requires replacing a dumb terminal with a PC or workstation and connecting them with a local area network. Such a move to desktop, client/server computing is currently being studied in most IS shops and is being implemented in many. This enables the construction of GUI programs, which is necessary in subsequent steps. A client/server architecture also allows off-loading of code from a server machine, where MIPS are typically expensive, to a client machine, where MIPS are essentially free.

Step 6 involves significant changes in the following areas:

- hardware and systems software

- applications, development, and maintenance architectures

- users and management

These changes likely require significant investments and time. Hence, step 6 may prolong the entire migration. However, it can be argued that doing it "right" cuts overall migration program time.

Following the premise underlying Chicken Little of migrating in small, incremental steps, step 6 can begin at any time and can be taken in steps appropriate to the context. That is, a few PCs at a time might be installed and new software deployed at a rate that is appropriate for your situation.

Step 7: Incrementally Create and Install the Forward Database Gateway

At this point, you're ready to develop the forward database gateway. The gateway is intended to encapsulate the target DBMS and target database from the legacy applications and to permit the application and database migration steps to proceed independently.

The forward gateway is designed so that the legacy applications need not be altered in any way. It includes a translator that captures and converts all legacy database service calls from legacy applications on the mainframe into calls against the modern DBMS on the server machines. The conversion may require a complex mapping of the calls (e.g., one-to-many, many-to-many, or special-purpose procedures) and data translation. The gateway must also capture responses from the DBMS, possibly convert them, and direct the result to the appropriate requesting modules. The gateway can also be used to enhance or correct legacy applications immediately, rather than waiting for the application migration step. For example, the data and call translator can introduce new data formats, data edits, and integrity and error checking and correction that will later be done in target applications or interfaces.

In complex environments, it is entirely possible (indeed likely) that the legacy data management environment consists of multiple data managers—for example, VSAM files, IMS and IDMS DBMSs, and a variety of relational DBMSs. In these cases, the forward gateway must be capable of serving the applications that utilize one or more of these legacy data environments and enable them to successfully process against the target environment.

The forward database gateway evolves as the IS migration proceeds. As target applications are cut over and legacy applications are retired, the gateway's translation and redirection functions are reduced accordingly. To support the mapping and redirection functions, it may be necessary to implement *mapping tables*. Mapping tables are tables or directories that provide a mapping between legacy database service entities and their modern DBMS counterparts, as well as between legacy data items and their corresponding target data counterparts.

The tables can identify when complex mappings, such as mapping programs, are required.

Constructing a forward gateway can be very costly. It involves writing the gateway from scratch or tailoring a commercial gateway product to meet the migration requirements. For certain DBMSs, a general-purpose forward database gateway can be built. In some cases, constructing a forward database gateway can be very complex because of the low-level legacy database service calls, which may have semantics that are unimplementable in SQL.

Date (1987) discusses this point in the context of IMS to SQL conversion. However, in general we doubt the feasibility of correct and efficient mapping of DL/I calls to any modern DBMS calls and vice versa, notwithstanding the fact that such claims are made for some products. The reason for this belief is not only experience but also the fact that in IMS, application semantics are spread throughout the data structures and programs. Therefore, they cannot be extracted algorithmically. Such cases require a special-purpose gateway that handles calls on a case-by-case basis.

Some DBMS vendors provide forward database gateway functions, and other vendors specialize in them. For example, Computer Associates' Transparency software is intended to provide translation of native or legacy DBMS calls to IMS, VSAM, and DB2 to calls to their CA-Datacom DBMS. Other gateways, such as Information Builders' EDA/SQL, are specifically designed to handle numerous underlying data resource managers with a focus on heterogeneous integration. Chapter 10 discusses commercial gateways in more detail. As a last resort, you may need to extend a gateway product or roll your own.

The gateway must be installed in the legacy IS architecture between the application modules and the legacy database service in preparation for the database migration (step 8). As with most approaches that involve abstraction layers, a gateway can significantly impact IS performance because of the necessary translations and mappings, the additional layered calls, and so on. It must be carefully designed and thoroughly tested, keeping in mind that the composite IS (the legacy IS plus the target IS) is mission-critical and can never fail. Although the gateway may negatively impact performance since all calls must go through it, this must be compared with the alternatives (e.g., no migration or specific, hand-coded traps).

If it is determined that a forward database gateway is impractical, alternative methods such as a reverse database gateway (discussed in Section 2.3) may be more appropriate.

Step 8: Migrate the Legacy Database

The actual database migration requires *force-fitting* the legacy application modules to the target database to achieve the architecture illustrated in Figure 2.2. This involves installing the target DBMS on the server machines, implementing the schema resulting from step 4, migrating the legacy database to the target DBMS under the new schema, and using the gateway to support the legacy application calls. The forward database gateway may be useful in the database migration, as it contains relevant mapping and translation information. You will be downloading, scrubbing, converting, and uploading possibly large amounts of data. Products such as Apertus Technologies' Enterprise/Sync, IBM's Data Extractor Tool (DXT), and BMC Software's LoadPlus support some of these functions.

This step requires significant analysis because of the potentially enormous costs. Again, a number of products claim to support this step. But bear in mind, they were probably developed for more reasonable tasks, like scrubbing addresses according to post office regulations. That's an example of a very specific kind of information with well-defined formats. The products may not have been tested on applications as complex as those you face.

Cold Turkey database migration may be impractical for several reasons. The legacy database may be so large or complex that there is no effective one-step, Cold Turkey migration method. Even if a method exists, some databases are so large that the time required for migration is greater than that allowable for the system to be nonoperational. Such cases require an incremental database migration step. That's part of the general migration method for decomposable ISs, which we detail in Section 2.4.

Step 9: Incrementally Migrate the Legacy Applications

Choose and then migrate legacy modules, one (or more) at a time. Selection should be based on technical and organizational criteria. Which modules would be simplest to migrate? Which modules are the most important? This involves rewriting the legacy modules to run directly against the modern DBMS, as illustrated in Figure 2.3. A growing number of products can help with rewriting legacy code into target applications. For example, Seer Technologies' High Productivity System (HPS) assists in converting IMS applications to SQL.

The target applications will run on a client machine in the target environment. They can be used to replace the legacy application modules that run on dumb terminals. The remaining legacy modules must continue to be used.

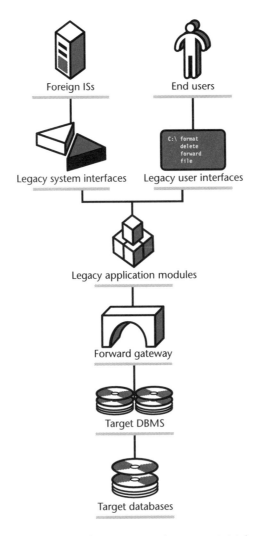

FIGURE 2.2 Forward migration architecture, initial state.

Step 10: Incrementally Migrate the Legacy Interfaces

Select and migrate legacy interfaces, one (or more) at a time. Selection should be based on principles similar to those in step 9. If a 4GL is used that supports application and interface development, interface and application migration might be coordinated. This involves rewriting the legacy user and system interfaces to run directly against the modern DBMS. In designing target interfaces, keep in mind that

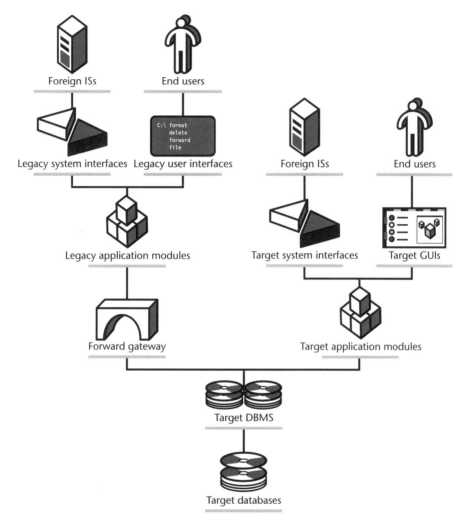

FIGURE 2.3 Forward migration architecture, intermediate state.

interfaces should be related to the business processes, not to individual applications.

The target interfaces will run on a client machine in a 4GL/GUI environment on the desktop. They can be used to replace the legacy interfaces that run on dumb terminals. The remaining legacy interfaces must continue to be used. An IS gateway (discussed in Section 1.8) could be used here to support interface migration.

Step 11: Incrementally Cut Over to the Target IS

Cutting over to the new IS involves cutover operations to the forward gateway and to the post-migration target database, applications, and interfaces on client/server machines. Then the legacy components can be discarded. When the last module is cut over and no legacy modules are in use, the forward database gateway can be discarded.

If no legacy components remain or require accesses to or from target components, the costly legacy environment, including the mainframe and the dumb terminals, can be discarded. The resulting target IS is illustrated in Figure 2.1.

The cutover can begin as soon as the database migration is complete. It continues as applications are transitioned and can be extended indefinitely. For example, it may be economical to run a bank branch or telephone office on the legacy IS for a year after others have transitioned if it is to be shut down or sold, thus losing the migration investment. Using the forward database gateway, legacy IS modules and their interfaces can be operational simultaneously with the corresponding target IS modules and their interfaces as long as required.

2.3 REVERSE MIGRATION METHOD FOR DECOMPOSABLE LEGACY ISs

Whereas forward migration involves a Cold Turkey transition of the database before accompanying applications, reverse migration involves the database transition in one final, Cold Turkey step (after the applications). It involves a reverse database gateway that aids a Chicken Little migration of the applications and their interfaces before the Cold Turkey database migration. It is called a *reverse* migration because target application calls must be migrated in the reverse direction, back onto the legacy database, until the legacy database is subsequently migrated.

Compared with forward migration, reverse migration permits more time to prepare for the database migration. Specifically, it permits you to determine the minimal amount of legacy data to migrate, as recommended in Chapter 1. Gateway capabilities may be added "just in time." However, as with forward migration, a Cold Turkey database migration and other limitations render the reverse migration method of limited applicability. But reverse migration principles remain important since they are required in all subsequent migration methods.

> A reverse migration redirects target application calls back to the legacy database until the legacy is migrated.

The reverse migration method is similar in most steps to the forward method (recall that both deal with decomposable ISs). The numbers of those steps that are different are shown in color in the following list:

The Chicken Little Steps

1. Incrementally analyze the legacy IS.
2. Incrementally decompose the legacy IS structure.
3. Incrementally design the target interfaces.
4. Incrementally design the target applications.
5. Incrementally design the target database.
6. Incrementally install the target environment.
7. Incrementally create and install the reverse database gateway.
8. Incrementally migrate the legacy applications.
9. Incrementally migrate the legacy interfaces.
10. Migrate the legacy database.
11. Incrementally cut over to the target IS.

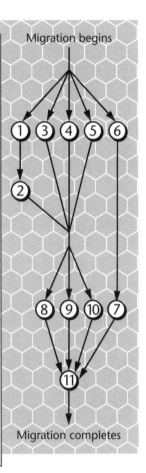

We'll discuss only those steps that differ from those of the forward migration method just discussed in Section 2.2.

Step 7: Incrementally Create and Install the Reverse Database Gateway

In this step we develop the reverse database gateway. The reverse database gateway includes a translator that captures and converts all calls to the modern DBMS from target applications and maps them into calls to the legacy database service. It must also capture, translate, and direct responses from the legacy database service to the appropriate modules.

The functions of and challenges in developing a reverse gateway are similar to those of the forward gateway (i.e., potentially complex mappings). As the IS migration proceeds, the reverse gateway must be modified. Initially, it may support one target application module. Incrementally, it supports more target application modules until all are supported, thereby completely encapsulating the legacy database service. It contracts as the target applications are migrated to access the target database directly.

As with the forward database gateway, the reverse database gateway will require mapping tables or directories, data and call conversion, and extended functionality. Also, there are many alternatives for constructing a reverse database gateway. For example, you could hand-code functions as needed, build a general-purpose reverse database gateway, or adapt commercial products. Hand-coded reverse database gateways may be appropriate for small IS migrations. However, a general-purpose reverse database gateway may be more appropriate for large IS migrations.

Some products provide reverse database gateway functions. For example, SQL Solutions' RMS Gateway product provides translation between DEC's RMS (files) and various RDBMSs. Oracle's SQL*Net and SQL*Connect provide translation from SQL to DB2, SQL/DS, RMS (files), and IMS. Information Builders' EDA/SQL provides translation among more than 50 DBMSs and file systems in client/server environments. Cross Access's product provides similar translation among more than 15 DBMSs and file systems. Apertus Technologies' Enterprise/Access product provides reverse gateway services. Most of these products do not support data integrity, transactions (i.e., updates), or query optimization. None of them supports all three. They also require that the calling applications be aware that they are calling a gateway and not a DBMS directly. This will require changes to all target applications once the gateway is removed.

The reverse database gateway must be installed in the migration architecture between the target application modules and the legacy database service, as illustrated in Figure 2.4. It then becomes a vital component in the migration and operation of the mission-critical IS.

Step 8: Incrementally Migrate the Legacy Applications

Using the reverse gateway, map the target application modules onto the legacy database to achieve the architecture illustrated in Figure

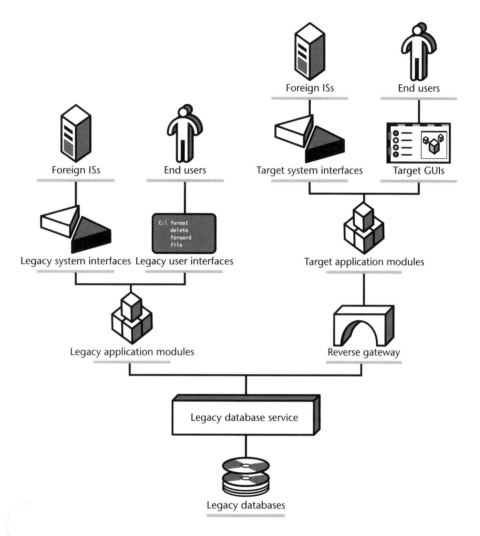

FIGURE 2.4 Reverse migration architecture, intermediate state.

2.4. Legacy modules should be selected and migrated one (or more) at a time. This step is similar to step 5 in the forward migration method except that, here, target application modules initially run against the reverse gateway.

The target applications will run on a client machine in the target environment on the desktop. They can be used to replace the legacy application modules. The remaining legacy modules must continue to be used until they too complete migration.

Step 11: Incrementally Cut Over to the Target IS

This step is similar to the forward migration step 11, except that the reverse migration cutover is more constrained and, consequently, of higher risk. The forward migration architecture can simultaneously support legacy and target applications. This provides flexibility as to how and when to cut over the IS. In the reverse migration method, once the legacy database is migrated, the legacy applications can no longer be used. Hence, the database, applications, and interface cutovers must be coordinated and must conclude simultaneously. This may place severe constraints on the cutover, since the IS is mission-critical and can be nonoperational for only a very short time.

2.4 GENERAL MIGRATION METHOD

As we mentioned earlier, the forward and reverse migration methods, while straightforward, aren't generally adequate individually to migrate most decomposable legacy ISs. The problem is that the database migration step is not adequately incremental in either method. The flexibility, hence applicability, of a migration method increases when all steps are incremental.

> A general migration makes use of both a forward and a reverse gateway and can proceed with any subset of IS functions and corresponding data.

In this section, we present a general migration method for all decomposable legacy ISs. It is a combination of the forward and reverse methods, which means it uses both a reverse database gateway and a forward database gateway. This permits the database migration step to be incremental and parallel with the other steps.

Following our Chicken Little strategy, IS migration can proceed by selecting, as iteration increments, any appropriate subset of IS functions and corresponding data, or vice versa.

For simplicity, we describe only the key differences with the forward and reverse migration methods already described. This includes some extra planning for the target database (step 5), in-depth discussions of the database gateway and the incremental migration of the legacy database (steps 7 and 8), and, finally, some words on how these changes affect migration of the legacy applications and cutover (steps 9 and 11). These steps are indicated in color in the following list.

The Chicken Little Steps

1. Incrementally analyze the legacy IS.
2. Incrementally decompose the legacy IS structure.
3. Incrementally design the target interfaces.
4. Incrementally design the target applications.
5. Incrementally design the target database.
6. Incrementally install the target environment.
7. Incrementally create and install the database gateway.
8. Incrementally migrate the legacy database.
9. Incrementally migrate the legacy applications.
10. Incrementally migrate the legacy interfaces.
11. Incrementally cut over to the target IS.

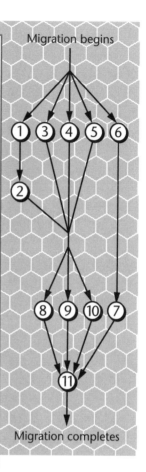

Step 5: Incrementally Design the Target Database

The legacy database must be logically partitioned to facilitate incremental database migration. Subsets of the legacy database that are sufficiently separable to be transitioned independently to the target database should be identified. For each subset, the target database schema (i.e., apply step 5 of the reverse migration method) should be designed so that the subset can be integrated into the target database. The mapping tables must be designed to reflect the location—legacy or target database—of all database elements.

Step 7: Incrementally Create and Install the Database Gateway

Unlike the reverse and forward methods, this migration may require simultaneously supporting portions of the corresponding legacy and target applications and databases. Throughout the migration process, the operational mission-critical IS will be some *composite* of legacy and target ISs, as illustrated in Figure 2.5. The gateway environment must support this composite; therefore, it must have characteristics of both forward and reverse gateways.

Additionally, complex layered information management functionality within the gateway is likely to be necessary. For example, it must ensure that update integrity be maintained on any part of the legacy database that is replicated in the target database. If a data item in the legacy database is updated, the corresponding target data item may be required to be updated accordingly within a given time. Such correspondences must be identified, expressed in interdatabase dependencies (i.e., conditions under which legacy database updates must be reflected in the target database, and vice versa), and maintained by the gateway. This coordination role of the gateway is similar to the transaction management role of a distributed DBMS. That is, it may involve distributed transactions, two-phase commit (2PC) or corollary protocols, and other transaction processing components.

This step is incremental in that the gateway functions vary throughout the migration. At the beginning of the migration, when the target database is empty, and at the end, when the legacy database is empty, there is little for the gateway to do. When many legacy and target components are operating simultaneously, the gateway must maintain all the interdatabase dependencies. Failure to do so at all or within adequate performance bounds may cause the mission-critical, composite IS to fail.

The gateway consists of at least four components:

- the forward database gateway

- the reverse database gateway

- a mapping table

- a coordinator

Since the potential mappings are more complex than in the forward and reverse database gateways, mapping tables will be correspondingly more sophisticated. It may be useful to maintain other descriptive data to assist with the migration. This metadata may form a small migration database that could be supported by the target DBMS. If the database mappings are sufficiently complex, the migration database may contain a schema that integrates those of the legacy and target databases, as is done in distributed DBMSs (Özsu and Valduriez 1991). On the other hand, application requirements may vary from instantaneous consistency to eventual consistency to no consistency required. Indeed, the gateway bears strong similarity to a general-purpose distributed DBMS plus a data dictionary/directory service.

The coordinator manages all gateway functions. On the basis of the location of the data being accessed and the relevant interdatabase dependencies, all given in the migration database, the coordinator must map calls from the legacy and target applications to one or more of the following: the legacy database, the target database, the reverse gateway, or the forward gateway. The alternatives are illustrated in Figure 2.5. Calls from legacy modules can be directed to the legacy database service, without translation, and to the target DBMS via the forward database gateway. Calls from target modules can be directed to the legacy database service via the reverse database gateway and to the target DBMS, without translation. The gateway may also need to combine responses from both database services and map them to either or both legacy and target applications.

The most challenging requirement for the coordinator is to ensure the interdatabase dependencies for updates as well as for queries mixed with the updates. A 2PC protocol (Skeen 1982) could be used by both the legacy and target DBMSs and by the gateway coordinator, as is done in distributed DBMSs (Elmagarmid 1992, Özsu and Valduriez 1991).

In an IBM mainframe environment, CICS can perform the coordinator role and both DB2 and IMS support 2PC; hence distributed transactions or distributed TP monitors such as Tuxedo are easily supported. However, most legacy database services or flat-file environments such as VSAM do not support 2PC. To guarantee that the interdatabase dependencies are maintained, 2PC might be hand-coded into the application modules. This exotic and difficult workaround is described in Breibart's article (1990).

Alternatively, the user can decompose a distributed transaction into two transactions, each updating only one database. If either transaction fails to commit, under some restricted conditions application logic can perform a compensating transaction to return the database to a consistent state. Compensating transactions are discussed by Garcia-Molina and Salem (1987) and Wachter and Reuter

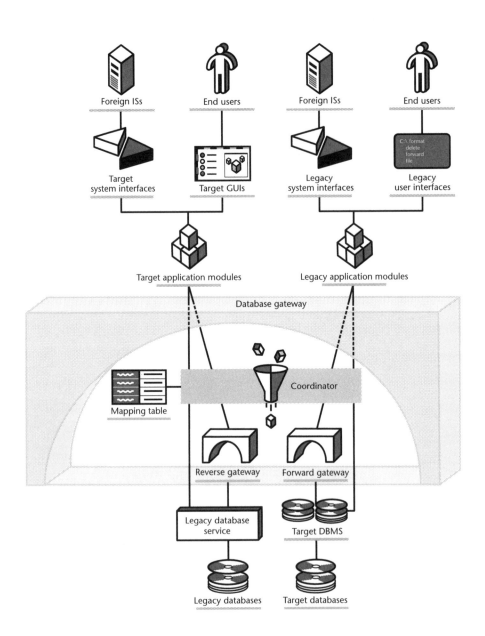

FIGURE 2.5 Decomposable legacy IS migration architecture.

(1992). Such compensations should be considered as a last resort and often are, since you then rely on your programming staff and these compensating transactions, which are simply other applications, for the consistency of your database. It has taken decades to move from this position to being able to count on the DBMS for consistency and reliability. To take such a step, necessitated by the lack of technical solutions, is a step backward in time and progress.

Another alternative that alleviates the application programmers from such concerns is to develop distributed transaction support in the coordinator, based on existing and special-purpose components (e.g., build the coordinator on the target DBMS that might also support distributed transactions). Besides providing 2PC protocols and distributed transaction management, the legacy database service must also be augmented with other transaction support, including transaction commit and abort, rollback, and compensation. This will be one of the most complex technical challenges in the migration and should be left to expert DBMS developers. Because it is so challenging, current gateway products do not support this coordinator function. You might consider paying a transaction processing vendor to build it for you. Although costly and risky, the benefits of building a coordinator may be more considerable than might initially be thought. The longer the gateway is used, the greater the benefits of implementing distributed transactions support, since it is amortized over a longer productive period.

> Transaction support is one of the most complex technical challenges in the migration.

IS migration will become a way of life for most organizations. Hence, distributed, flexible transaction support, as described above, will become a critical component of the target environment, and supporting products will begin appearing on the market. For example, existing commercial transaction processing monitor products support some degree of the required functionality.

As the distributed transaction architecture is put in place with respect to the database gateways, decisions must be made concerning the characteristics of the transaction models that will be implemented. Such decisions include whether distributed updates that span the legacy and target environments should be *synchronous*—that is, should they require 2PC or corollary protocols to ensure that all updates act as described above with respect to commit or rollback?—or *asynchronous* in nature.

With an asynchronous transaction model, transactions are decomposed into subtransactions. Each subtransaction (within the context of the overall transaction) may commit or roll back independently of the other subtransactions, but in accordance with the rules of the specific asynchronous transaction model. One such model is a *chained transaction model*, in which each subtransaction commits, but the failure of any subsequent subtransaction does not require the repeat of previously committed subtransactions. Only the subtransaction that has failed needs to be restarted.

Characteristics such as the degree of distribution of the target environment (and, for that matter, that of the legacy environment as well) help determine what sort of distributed transaction model might be required. For example, widely distributed environments, such as target environments with many different servers, may require a mix of synchronous and asynchronous transaction capabilities. Data elements that must be kept in constant coordination between legacy and target environments may be updated using synchronous protocols, while the propagation of other updates, like updating the user database on all servers, across the entire target enterprise may be done in a chained, asynchronous manner.

Further information about complex transaction models may be found in Gray and Reuter's book (1993).

Step 8: Incrementally Migrate the Legacy Database

One (or more) independent legacy database subsets (identified in step 5) must be selected on the basis of technical and organizational criteria. The corresponding schema is implemented in the target DBMS by incrementally augmenting the current target schema.

The corresponding legacy database subset is then transitioned to the target DBMS. This might be aided with several potential migration or downloading tools found in the legacy database service, in the target DBMS, or in special-purpose products. The gateway could be extended to support database migration, since the migration database could contain metadata relevant for translation. The gateway must be enhanced to accommodate any new interdatabase dependencies that may have arisen from the migration of the current database subset. The dependencies must be characterized in the mapping table.

Database migration can use the following simple method. When the migration of some subset of the database is attempted, there are k old modules and $n - k$ new ones. The new applications use a reverse gateway to convert as needed from SQL to the legacy database service. The old applications use the forward gateway when needed to talk to the SQL DBMS.

A target distributed DBMS that supports fragments for database tables could be introduced. Hence, each table can be distributed, and a distribution criteria determines where individual records reside. For example, the following distribution criteria places young employees on machine 1 and old employees on machine 2.

```
distribute EMP
    to machine 1 where EMP.age < 30
    to machine 2 where EMP.age > = 30
```

Further suppose the distributed DBMS supports distributed transactions through 2PC. Most distributed DBMSs allow data to be stored in tables managed by other vendors' single-site DBMSs. This is accomplished by an SQL reverse gateway within the distributed DBMS that translates from SQL to the foreign vendors protocol.

Such software makes migration a breeze. Bring up the distributed DBMS with the initial distribution criteria:

```
old system:     everything
new system:     nothing
```

Legacy IS transactions are supported by converting legacy database accesses to SQL accesses that are processed by the distributed DBMS. If necessary, the distributed DBMS can route accesses to data not yet migrated using the reverse gateway to the old DBMS. Over time the migration is accomplished by changing the distribution criteria in small increments until the final result is achieved:

```
old system:     nothing
new system:     everything
```

The cutover step (step 11) must be invoked to support the related database cutover that brings the migrated database into operational use.

Step 9: Incrementally Migrate the Legacy Applications

Select and migrate legacy modules one (or more) at a time. This is similar to step 8 of the reverse migration method. A target module will run against the gateway until the gateway is no longer required, that is, until the corresponding target database has been migrated and no coordination is needed. Then the target module can be transitioned from the gateway to the target DBMS.

Step 11: Incrementally Cut Over to the Target IS

Coordinate all the incremental, and possibly parallel, migrations of subsets of the legacy IS (e.g., environment, database, applications, and interfaces), making them operational while ensuring that the composite IS meets its mission-critical requirements. This step is similar in nature to the final steps of the corresponding forward and reverse migration methods. This step offers a wider range of alternatives to avoid problems that arise in those steps.

A fundamental difference in the general migration from the forward and reverse migrations is the need to coordinate updates between the legacy and target databases. Throughout the migration, some, or all, of the legacy database on the mainframe will be operational simultaneously with the target database on the database server(s). Hence, there may be distributed transactions that perform updates in both systems using a 2PC protocol. At the end of the cutover process, the distributed DBMS (suggested in step 8) can be discarded or used in cutting over the next portion of the database.

The cutover must deal with incrementally retiring subsets of the legacy IS that have been migrated after the corresponding target IS subset is operational. The legacy subsets should be retired only if they are of no further use. This permits the gateway to be simplified accordingly. A legacy database subset is no longer of use only when it is strictly independent from all other database subsets and no legacy application accesses it. Because of the interdependence within legacy databases and between legacy databases and their applications, this may be difficult to judge. For example, what may appear as two or more logically distinct data groupings may be stored physically as one highly interdependent data and index structure. Such considerations significantly complicate the cutover step. This may result in the requirement to maintain legacy components and the gateway for some time.

2.5 CLOSING REMARKS

In this chapter, we've discussed methods that might be used for the migration of decomposable legacy information systems. While both forward and reverse migration approaches have their own merits, it is entirely likely you will need to combine them, resulting in an environment like that shown in Figure 2.5. In most cases, database migration will require both forward and reverse gateways.

In the next chapter, we will look at a case study of migrating a decomposable legacy information system to a target client/server architecture using the modern software. The case study follows our Chicken Little general migration method for decomposable legacy information systems.

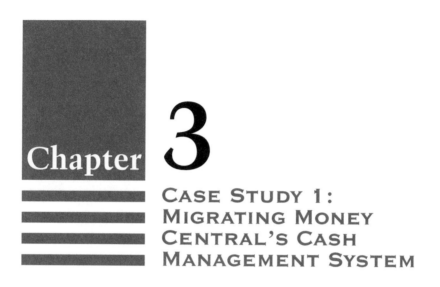

Chapter 3

CASE STUDY 1: MIGRATING MONEY CENTRAL'S CASH MANAGEMENT SYSTEM

I n this chapter, we discuss a case study representative of the migration of decomposable legacy ISs. We had the opportunity to construct a migration plan for the cash management system (CMS) for a large money center bank. We'll call this bank "Money Central" throughout the chapter. This assignment was a perfect opportunity to develop and validate our Chicken Little method for decomposable ISs. This chapter describes CMS, our analysis, and our migration plan.

3.1 OUR BACKGROUND RESEARCH

CMS supports check processing and other specialized services for Money Central's large corporate customers. For example, CMS provides a service known as *zero balance accounts*, whereby Money Central notifies the customer of all the checks that are processed during a given day and allows the customer to cover the exact amount of these checks with a single deposit. This enables the customer to apply the minimum possible capital to cover liabilities, and only at the exact time that the capital is needed.

A second CMS service is the *reconciliation of cleared checks*. The customer provides Money Central with an electronic feed of all the checks written each day. Money Central matches the issued checks against those that clear.

Money Central then indicates to the customer, again through an electronic feed, all checks that have cleared, as well as those still pending.

CMS performs *electronic funds transfers* between customer accounts. When the initiator or recipient of the transfer is another bank, the funds must be electronically received from or transmitted to the other bank. This requires connection to several electronic money transfer systems (e.g., Swift) as well as to the Federal Reserve bank.

CMS SERVICES
zero balance accounts
reconciliation of cleared checks
electronic funds transfers
lockbox operations
on-line query facility

CMS also supports *lockbox operations*, in which U.S. mail is received from a post office box and opened. CMS deposits the checks for the customer and renders an accounting. This service is appropriate for a customer who receives large numbers of checks in the mail, such as a landlord or a utility company.

CMS supports many other services that Money Central offers its corporate customers. As a final example, CMS has an *on-line query facility* that enables customers to check their account status and make transactions like the aforementioned funds transfer.

CMS includes 40 separate software modules that perform these functions, totaling approximately 8 million lines of code. Most of the code runs in a COBOL/CICS/VSAM environment. However, the connection to the Federal Reserve bank is implemented on a Tandem machine using TAL, the system programming language supported in that environment. Lockbox operations are provided on a DEC VAX and are written in C. These additional environments exist because the bank bought external software packages and then acquired the hardware to run them.

The majority of CMS was written in 1981. It has grown to process between 1 and 2 million checks in a batch processing run each night and approximately 300,000 on-line transactions each day. At the time of the project, most of CMS ran on an IBM 3090/400J with 120 spindles of DASD. Total on-line storage exceeds 100 gigabytes.

Like most legacy systems of large organizations, CMS is probably too complex for any group to understand in its entirety. Much of the CMS code provides interfaces to ISs elsewhere in the bank or in other organizations. These interfaces are not key CMS functions. To reduce the migration problem to one of manageable proportions, we removed from consideration modules that are not within the core function of CMS.

After discussion with application experts, we concluded that core functions of CMS were supported by the following three subsystems:

- Xcheck: 1 million lines of COBOL

- Xtransfer: 200,000 lines of COBOL

- Xcash: 500,000 lines of COBOL

Xcheck provides batch check processing and reconciliation. It also supports on-line transactions submitted by internal bank personnel from synchronous 3270 terminals. Xtransfer supports electronic funds transfer and delivers transactions to Xcheck when account updates are required. Xcash is an on-line system that supports inquiry and update to the Xcheck VSAM files from dial-up asynchronous terminals on customer premises. The terminals are typically IBM PCs.

We decided to exclude from consideration the software supporting the paper-processing operation (check sorting), which occurs before batch processing by Xcheck. Although this is a core function, it is a front-end, easily isolated module that contains vendor-supplied code particular to the check-sorting hardware. Because Money Central had no interest in new check sorters and was happy with this portion of the system, we ignored it. As a result, we concentrated exclusively on a migration plan for the 1.7 million lines of core CMS code listed above, ignoring the remaining 6.3 million lines of code.

3.2 ANALYSIS OF THE CMS CORE

We next began a detailed analysis of the CMS core. The purpose was to understand the application structure: the chunks of code that are not dependent on the rest of the system. A code analyzer would have helped to extract the desired macro structure. In our exercise, we estimated the required structure by conversations with application experts.

The 1.7 million lines of CMS code had the following approximate composition.

Xcash: This system is composed of some 500 modules, each a separate on-line transaction. An average of 1,000 lines of COBOL supports each transaction. The actual work is performed by Xcheck update routines. An immediate conclusion was that this system should be reimplemented in a 4GL for deployment on a desktop. Compared with COBOL, a modern 4GL should achieve a factor of 10–20 code reduction. This results from being able to specify form definitions interactively using a "what you see is what you get" paradigm, rather than using in-line declarations. Although the actual code com-

For this planning phase of the case study, we conducted the application analysis over a three-day period in a small room deep in the Manhattan jungle. Eight legacy migration experts, five information technology managers, and five CMS experts sat around a table. We pored over printouts and had various chalk talks. There was considerable discussion. In essence, we relied on the knowledge of experts—the designer and chief developer of CMS. Each had spent over a decade solely on CMS. Some hotshot developers provided details on current status. The migration team hypothesized lots of analytical queries to our database of information on CMS's functions and data. The human experts responded with understandings, estimates, and intuition. If all CMS data and code, and the corresponding metadata and designs, were in a "CMS database," we might have had concrete answers to support the experts' intuition. In its absence, we went with what we had.

pression varies widely from application to application, the 10–20 figure is a good rule of thumb. As a result, there should be around 25,000–50,000 lines of 4GL code.

Some customers will choose to run the 4GL code on a desktop PC. Others won't want bank code running on their machines, instead preferring to use their PCs as dumb terminal emulators. Therefore, the bank must supply one or more *application servers* on which the 4GL application will run. Such application servers must be multithreaded. A variety of low-cost UNIX servers (*jelly beans*) make ideal candidates for deployment of this sort of code.

Xtransfer: This system provides a data entry facility for an operator to specify transactions for funds transfer, an auditing and message tracking facility, and an interface to several wire service systems. About 15% of this COBOL program is user interface code that should be rewritten in a 4GL; the remainder should be rewritten or ported to the new environment.

Xcheck: This system is the ultimate core of CMS. It consists of two portions, one for batch processing and one for on-line inquiry.

The on-line portion contains 250 on-line transactions for 3270 terminals on the desks of bank personnel. Each transaction is a separate program, averaging 1,000 lines, and uses 3270 protocols to communicate with dumb terminals. This portion of Xcheck should be rewritten in a 4GL. Of course, the bank must ensure that a PC is on every employee's desk, so that the rewritten Xcheck need only support a GUI interface for a PC and not a 3270 interface. Wide deployment of PCs is ongoing at the bank, and, in this case, a judicious acceleration of desktop hardware results in a simplified target software environment.

The transactions call a *kernel* to access and update the actual VSAM files. The kernel is a well-structured collection of modules totaling about 32,000 lines of COBOL. The kernel should be rewritten in C or perhaps a 4GL.

The batch processing portion of Xcheck consists of 294 modules, performing the following functions:

- Four modules access and update VSAM files. These are batch versions of the kernel mentioned above for the on-line portion. They total approximately 40,000 lines of COBOL.

- Forty modules prepare data for processing. These programs filter data and repair fields in records.

- There are 130 customer-specific report-generating and formatting programs.

- Eighty programs write internal bank files for audit purposes.

- Forty other programs produce assorted reports.

The last three classes of modules listed above all perform basic report generation. As such, 250 of the 294 modules should be rewritten using the SQL provided by the target DBMS, plus its report writer (available in all commercial DBMS packages). Note that we are not migrating any code at all; we are migrating functions that are being completely rewritten. This is the best form of reuse—reuse of function specifications but not reuse of code. The code can be tossed.

As a result of the above discussion, the batch portion of Xcheck consists of about

- 40,000 lines of kernel code that execute batch updates,

- 40,000 lines of *prep* code that execute before the batch run, and

- 250,000 lines of reporting code that should be rewritten.

Xcheck has about 300,000 lines of code that serve no current function.

3.3 THE CMS MIGRATION PLAN

Money Central was interested in a migration plan for CMS because it was a typical legacy IS. Since CMS costs around $16 million per year in hardware and related support costs, management was very interested in rightsizing.

Moreover, they were eager to move to a modern DBMS and evolve away from dependence on a single batch run implementing an *old-master/new-master* methodology. Bank customers are eager to know early in the day how much money will be coming into their accounts (from deposits or lockboxes) and how much will be going out (from cleared checks). In effect, customers want an *on-line* transaction system rather than a *batch* transaction system. Such features are incompatible with the existing batch-oriented system.

Money Central requested that we construct a migration plan satisfying the following constraints, which reflect real financial and business responsibilities in the client environment.

THE PLAN
1. Rewrite Xcash in a 4GL.
2. Rewrite Xtransfer in a 4GL.
3. Rewrite the on-line portion of Xcheck in a 4GL.
4. Migrate the reconciliation database to an SQL system.
5. Rewrite the data feeds and reports using SQL and a report writer.
6. Migrate the preparation code to the jelly bean environment.
7. Move the account data from VSAM to SQL.

- No migration step could require more than 10 person-years of development.

- No migration step could take more than one calendar year.

- Each migration step had to pay back its cost over a maximum of one year.

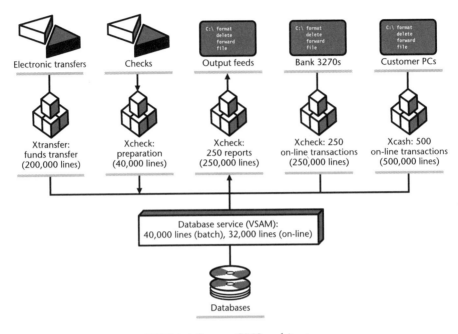

FIGURE 3.1 Legacy CMS architecture.

The following migration plan was constructed. Our starting point was the legacy CMS illustrated in Figure 3.1. Following Chicken Little principles, the migration plan decomposed the CMS migration into seven individual and incremental migrations, each for a relatively independent subset of CMS. Each migration applies the migration method for decomposable legacy ISs described in Section 2.4. The description below focuses on the seven migrations and how they intermix the critical database and application migration steps (steps 8 and 9) of the Chicken Little decomposable migration method.

Migration 1: Rewrite Xcash in a 4GL.

Xcash should run on client machines in the customer premises. The new 4GL code must be able to submit transactions coded in SQL to Xcheck over an LU 6.2 interface, so that the existing code can perform the actual VSAM inquiries and updates. This requires a reverse gateway, as illustrated in Figure 3.2. This migration requires less than the 10-person-year limit. Money Central management agreed to this because it made sense in terms of cost/performance and function. Xcash can do its job with minimal cost, and it will substitute cheap jelly bean cycles for expensive mainframe cycles.

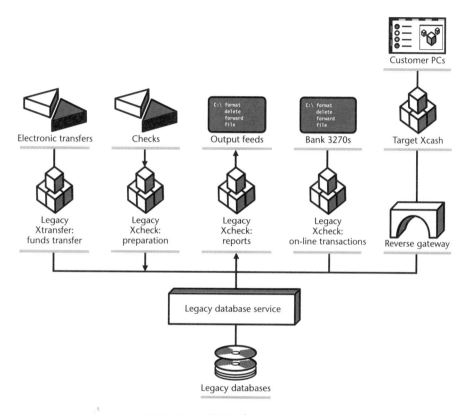

FIGURE 3.2 CMS after migration 1.

Migration 2: Rewrite Xtransfer in a 4GL.

Xtransfer should also be deployed on a PC. This migration was sold to management for the following reasons: it will take less than five person-years, will lower maintenance costs, and will consolidate the three versions of Xtransfer currently in operation.

Migration 3: Rewrite the on-line portion of Xcheck in a 4GL.

Again, the 4GL must be able to connect to the on-line kernel of Xcheck through LU 6.2. This step involves 12,500 lines of 4GL code that should be implementable within the 10-person-year constraint. The bank management agreed to this plan because they would be moving cycles from expensive machines to cheap machines. The result of this migration is illustrated in Figure 3.3.

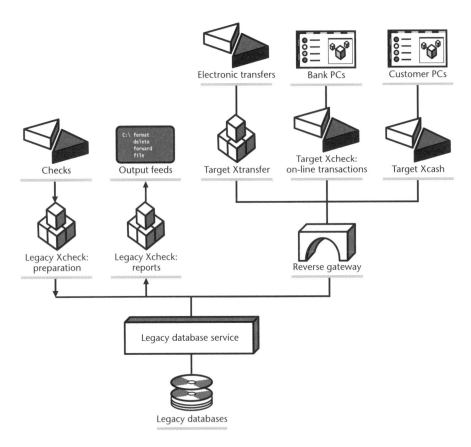

FIGURE 3.3 CMS after migration 3.

The batch processing code is somewhat more complex to migrate. The on-line kernel and the batch kernel must be combined and moved to a DBMS. Then 250 new reports and feeds must be constructed. In addition, the preparation code must be moved to cheaper hardware. This process was estimated at considerably more than 10 person-years, so it was broken into smaller increments.

Xcheck performs two services:

- account maintenance

- check reconciliation

After lengthy discussion, it was decided that these were the only separable components of the database. As a result, the migration plan with the least risk entailed migrating these two functions separately. In general, when a large

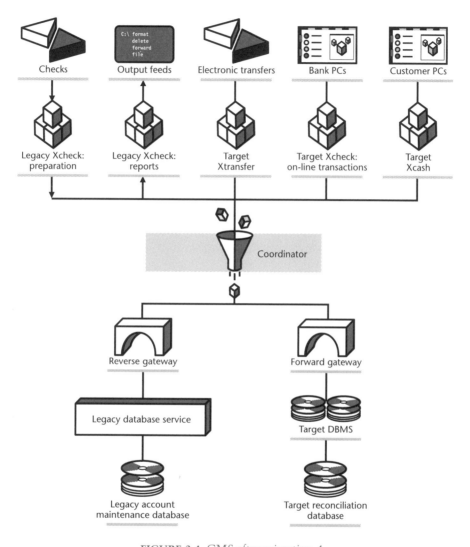

FIGURE 3.4 CMS after migration 4.

system performs multiple functions, it is a useful strategy to migrate the individual functions separately. Therefore the next migration is obvious.

Migration 4: Migrate the reconciliation database to an SQL system.

This migration results in a new reconciliation database running in parallel with the legacy database. It requires reverse and forward gateways and a coordinator, as illustrated in Figure 3.4.

Account balances remain in the legacy VSAM files. The coordinator must ensure that some information in transactions to be diverted to the SQL DBMS must also go into the legacy VSAM files. This can be done, because all reconciliation activity on each account can be put into a single, *aggregate* VSAM transaction, which can then be inserted into the batch stream. This is an example of the legacy and target databases running in parallel, as described in step 8 of the general migration method (Section 2.4). The majority of the database is moved from the old to the new environment. However, the old environment is still the *system of record*. This is ensured by the coordinator.

Migration 5: Rewrite the data feeds and reports using SQL and a report writer.

Data feeds and reports that involve both reconciliation and account balances must be modified to work correctly in the hybrid environment illustrated in Figure 3.4.

Discussion with CMS experts and back-of-the-envelope calculations convinced us that the fourth and fifth migrations could be accomplished in a 10-person-year period. Moreover, the project could be sold to management on the basis of three factors. 1) Reconciliation information would be available earlier. 2) Computing cycles would be moved from expensive to cheaper hardware. 3) A portion of the database would be moved from expensive mainframe DASD to cheaper DASD.

Migration 6: Migrate the preparation code to the jelly bean environment.

The 40,000 lines of preparation code must be migrated from the mainframe to the cheaper jelly bean environment—the UNIX servers. It is conceivable that the current code could be ported. A more plausible scenario is that it be rewritten as an on-line application. Even if a total rewrite is required, this can be easily accomplished in the 10-person-year time constraint. It will offload mainframe cycles; however, the payback from this particular migration may be less than those from the other migrations. This is the only migration in which a one-year payback is questionable. We saw no way to avoid violating the ground rules for this particular migration.

At the end of the sixth migration, the account balances remain in the VSAM system and only about 72,000 lines of kernel VSAM update code actually access this data. This remaining database must be transitioned as the last migration.

Migration 7: Move the account data from VSAM to SQL.

This final migration is trivial to justify. It would allow the mainframe to be retired, resulting in a large hardware savings, and would provide data liberation for the legacy data. Any program using SQL could access the data.

3.4 CMS CUTOVER ISSUES

Each migration in the above plan introduces serious cutover problems. It is impossible for CMS to be down for more than a few hours. If the new system fails to work for any reason, the old system must resume operation immediately. Any failure to accomplish a smooth transition would be a cause for immediate dismissal of the Money Central personnel involved.

Cutovers that entail rewritten applications are straightforward. Beginning with the old system, you can migrate users, one by one. Hence, at any given point in the cutover process, some fraction is running the legacy application while the rest run the corresponding target application. IS personnel can move users at whatever rate can be accommodated. Recovery from a catastrophe can be accomplished by restoring the old application code.

The database migration and cutover steps proposed for decomposable ISs (steps 8 and 11 in Section 2.4) pose serious problems for CMS. There is considerable overhead in using a forward gateway to map DBMS calls in the old system to SQL and a reverse gateway to map them back to the old DBMS. This would seriously tax the IBM machine currently running CMS. In addition, distributed DBMS software with these features was not yet widely available or robust enough for Money Central's requirements. (This situation has since changed.) The IBM mainframe is already overloaded with non-CMS applications and CMS. Any additional processing required by a CMS migration gateway will just make it worse.

Because of these problems, we proposed an alternate approach for database migration and cutover. To migrate any portion of the database, that portion would be replicated in the target database—that is, some group of objects would appear in both the legacy and target databases. It is necessary to identify all transactions that update those replicated objects and execute them twice: once on the legacy database and once on the target. Depending on whether they originate in 4GL code or COBOL, they will execute directly against the database or use a forward or reverse gateway.

In essence, the target database is brought up in parallel with the legacy database. For a while, duplicate transactions are performed. Subsequently, data items would be removed from the legacy database and the duplication of transactions would be turned off. The cutover of those objects would then be complete. The replication of an object does not require a distributed DBMS or the cascaded use of a gateway. Hence, it will require less overhead on a crowded mainframe and was chosen as the better alternative. However, the gateway must support update consistency.

3.5   CLOSING REMARKS

The CMS migration plan consists of two major steps:

- Incrementally migrate the legacy applications. CMS is a decomposable IS. Therefore, modules can be peeled off one by one and moved to a new environment in manageable-sized chunks.

- Incrementally migrate the legacy database. The database can be divided into multiple pieces, which can be migrated one by one. Although cutover is a problem, it can be accomplished using the brute-force method of running the two databases in parallel.

After completing these two steps, we were left with a small core that had manageable complexity and could be moved as the final step. It is our assertion that most complex ISs can be peeled in this fashion. If CMS's architecture had been poorly designed—for example, if Xcash had performed its own updates instead of calling Xcheck—then the core would have been larger. In this case, we speculate that the restructuring of multiple kernels into a single kernel would have been the appropriate step (i.e., in migration 3).

> Migrate the data; toss the code.

Finally, note that our migration plan is an incremental rewrite of CMS and not incremental restructuring. Although much interest has been expressed in reengineering legacy ISs, our case study indicated that virtually all code would be better rewritten using modern tools, especially 4GLs, report writers, and relational DBMS query languages. There may be legacy ISs for which restructuring is a larger part of the migration plan. However, our experience with CMS did not indicate any significant use of this technique.

Our migration plan was initiated shortly after it was approved by management for funding and commitment of other resources. It proceeded for less than a year before it was terminated, largely for administrative reasons. The division responsible for CMS was merged into another division. The new management had a broader IS mandate, one that redirected its priorities and was adverse to a migration plan that targeted UNIX. As a result, they stopped funding the project. In spite of this failure, the Chicken Little approach to software evolution has been widely applauded within Money Central and is expected to be used in future IS migration projects.

Chapter 4

MIGRATING SEMIDECOMPOSABLE LEGACY ISs

W̲e noted in Chapter 1 that semidecomposable legacy ISs—
ISs in which the application and database services aren't
separable from one another—present additional challenges with respect to the migration process.

The good news, though, is that our methodology introduced in
Chapter 2 is tailorable to such ISs. By adjusting the migration steps to
account for this semidecomposable nature, the transition process may
proceed in much the same way as with decomposable systems. That
is, the use of gateways, incremental steps of varying complexity and
size, and other characteristics of our methodology will help move the
legacy environment to an open target IS.

The bad news, however, is that the technical challenges are
greater. For example, since the legacy information system is semidecomposable, it may be more difficult or impossible to separate as
many legacy interface, application, or database components. Hence,
migration increments may be larger with correspondingly higher risk.

4.1 SEMIDECOMPOSABLE IS IDIOSYNCRASIES

In terms of legacy IS migration, semidecomposable ISs are more complex than
decomposable ISs. The applications and database services of a semidecompos-

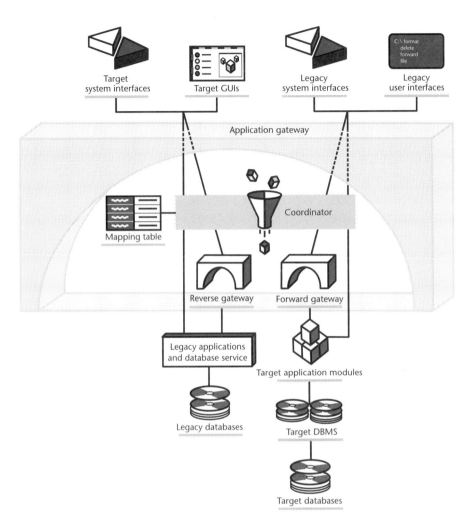

FIGURE 4.1 Semidecomposable legacy IS migration architecture.

able IS are coupled so closely that it is almost impossible to separate them for migration purposes. If they are separable, within reasonable effort and risk, then the decomposable migration strategy should be used. It's possible, too, that some portions could be separated for decomposable migration with acceptable effort and risk, but others will be too costly and risky, especially assuming the components will be retired after the migration.

The migration architecture for a semidecomposable legacy IS contains an application gateway placed between the interfaces and the legacy and target ISs, as illustrated in Figure 4.1. This gateway maps application calls from the interface modules to application calls in the legacy and target applications. This method applies the reverse and forward migration methods, described in Section 2.4, but here they are directed to the application call level.

> Semidecomposable ISs are more difficult to migrate because the applications and database services are so tightly coupled.

4.2 THE SEMIDECOMPOSABLE IS MIGRATION METHOD

The migration method for semidecomposable legacy ISs is intended to produce a target decomposable IS. (See Figure 2.1 for the architecture of decomposable ISs.) The basic migration model for these situations is largely the same as the decomposable IS model discussed in Chapter 2. In this chapter we'll focus on the extensions to the migration method necessary for semidecomposable legacy ISs.

The steps for migrating semidecomposable ISs are as follows:

The Chicken Little Steps

1. Incrementally analyze the legacy IS.
2. Incrementally decompose the legacy IS structure.
3. Incrementally design the target interfaces.
4. Incrementally design the target applications.
5. Incrementally design the target database.
6. Incrementally install the target environment.
7. Incrementally create and install the application gateway.
8. Incrementally migrate the legacy database.
9. Incrementally migrate the legacy applications.
10. Incrementally migrate the legacy interfaces.
11. Incrementally cut over to the target IS.

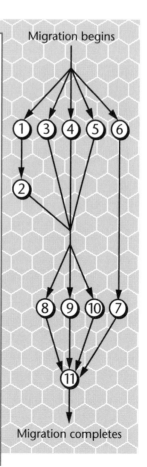

The Chicken Little strategy suggests that you migrate one or more components of the appropriate size, considering effort, risk, and technical challenges,

> The migration method for semidecomposable legacy ISs is intended to produce a target decomposable IS.

among other factors. We recommend the separate migration of environment, interface, application, and database components, as suggested in the above steps. We also recommend the incremental migration of each such component. For example, the database component should be migrated in separable subcomponents. That is what we mean by *incrementally* in all of the above steps.

The flowchart indicates how the steps can proceed. You can start with analyzing the legacy IS (step 1), designing the target IS (any of steps 3, 4, or 5), or installing the target environment (step 6). You can decompose the legacy IS (step 2) after you've completed step 1. To install the gateway (step 7), you must have already installed the target environment (step 6). You can migrate the interfaces, applications, or database (steps 8, 9, 10), or install the gateway (step 7), in any order. When you have completed those steps, you are ready to cut over the IS (step 11). This flow of steps is for each increment to be migrated, so the entire flow is repeated for each such increment.

Step 1: Incrementally Analyze the Legacy IS

The first step is more complex than that for decomposable legacy IS migration because of the increased complexity of the architecture. The binding of applications and database services makes analysis much more difficult. However, as thorough an analysis as appropriate is necessary for step 2. You need to find as many dependencies as you can among the applications, and between the applications and the database service. This will simplify the migration that otherwise must support all the dependencies.

Step 2: Incrementally Decompose the Legacy IS Structure

Be careful. The decomposition of the legacy IS structure may be too complex or may introduce too much risk. In the worst case, the legacy IS will remain in its original form. Although this will complicate the gateway, increase costs, reduce performance, and add risk to the overall migration effort, the retention of the legacy environment in its status quo form just before the transition program begins will isolate the risk to the actual migration steps themselves.

The legacy system restructuring and code modification called for in this step have their own risks. For example, they can negatively affect performance as a result of heavy-duty modifications on applications and subsystems that will be moved later anyway. In effect, the characteristics of any given environment dictate whether the risk will be divided into preparatory steps and then migration steps, or handled exclusively during the transition itself.

There are a growing number of commercial tools for "slicing and dicing" legacy code. The analytical capabilities of these tools may be useful. They may even provide assistance in modest restructuring to improve modularity. However, we do not believe at all that these tools permit you to extract legacy code for reuse outside the source legacy application, as some of their vendors claim. You should ask these vendors to prove their claims in detail before embarking on such a project.

Our advice here is to modify the legacy IS to improve modularity and thus decomposability as long as the effort and related risks are small. After all, you hope to discard the legacy modules in the not-too-distant future. Much more effort in this area may be justifiable should you plan to significantly prolong the life of your legacy IS.

Step 3: Incrementally Design the Target Interfaces

Step 3 designs the end-user and system interfaces for the target IS. To do this, you must develop an interface migration plan from the legacy, through the composite, to the target IS. To ease the migration of end users, it may be helpful to use an IS gateway (see Section 1.8). It provides a single composite IS interface, which will support both legacy and target interfaces and assist with the migration between them.

Step 4: Incrementally Design the Target Applications

The target applications are incrementally designed on the basis of the requirements resulting from the analysis in step 1. This step is the same as step 4 of the decomposable migration model (Section 2.2). The applications that will run on the target platforms must be designed in accordance with the business rules that will be supported in the target environment.

Incorporation of additional requirements or target functions increases the risk of failure. Acceptance of varying levels of risk comes into play at this point. A low-risk requirement would be to add a new interface (e.g., GUI). A high-risk change would be to add another significant function or new data entities. These latter changes require significant technical challenges, whereas the interface may not.

In our experience, it has been almost impossible to develop the target IS without accepting new requirements. Hence, we strongly recommend that you control the risk: separate technical risk resulting from migration from that resulting from additional requirements. In isolated components that demand requirements changes, the risk may necessarily be higher—the target IS would not be acceptable without them.

Step 5: Incrementally Design the Target Database

Step 5 requires the incremental design of the target database. The less knowledge there is about the legacy database or application structure, the more likely it is that the legacy and target databases will have to run in parallel. This increases the importance and difficulty of coordinating the databases and defining and maintaining the correctness criteria for the composite, operational IS.

Step 6: Incrementally Install the Target Environment

This step—incremental installation of the target environment—is the same as step 6 of the migration method for decomposable systems (Section 2.2). Identify the requirements for the target environment on the basis of total target IS requirements. Treat the target environment as if it were being developed from scratch, exclusive of the migration-oriented issues.

Typically the target environment consists of a desktop computer for each target IS user and appropriate server machines. This requires replacing a dumb terminal with a PC or workstation and connecting them with a local area network. Once you've selected your target environment, test it and then install it incrementally.

Installing the target environment involves significant changes across the board. You'll have to make substantial investments in hardware and systems software. You'll have to rethink and restrategize the applications, development, and maintenance architectures. Moreover, users and management will need time to adjust to the new environment. In other words, step 6 may prolong the entire migration.

But remember that the Chicken Little method offers you several advantages. You can begin step 6 at any time, and you can install the target environment in increments of your own choosing. That is, a few PCs at a time might be installed and new software deployed at a rate that is appropriate for your organization.

Step 7: Incrementally Create and Install the Application Gateway

This may be the most technically challenging step. The application gateway captures legacy and target application calls from legacy and target interfaces. The gateway either passes them unchanged to the legacy and target applications (respectively) or translates them to target and legacy application calls (respectively). It must capture the corresponding results, translate them if needed, and direct them back to the appropriate interfaces. The application gateway must coordinate target and legacy updates when the two simultaneously support duplicate applications or data. Application coordination could be similar to but more complex than database coordination described for the database gateway in step 7 of the general migration model (Section 2.4).

Database technology has provided the theory and technology for database coordination, in terms of update. We know of no such theory or technology for application coordination, although it is a burgeoning area because, in part, of the popularity of the object-oriented paradigm. In that domain, the question is not, How do you coordinate data? but rather, How do you coordinate objects? Until such solutions are provided, we recommend simple extensions of database concurrency control techniques. Please refer to Gray and Reuter (1993) and Özsu and Valduriez (1991) for more information.

Step 8: Incrementally Migrate the Legacy Database

At this point you can begin the incremental migration of the database. It may be useful to augment the gateway to assist with database migration, because the required mapping information may be in the gateway's migration database.

The Remaining Steps: Application Migration, Interface Migration, and Cutover

Steps 9 through 11 (incremental legacy applications migration, incremental legacy interfaces migration, and incremental target IS cutover) are the same as steps 9 through 11 of the decomposable migration method (Section 2.2). For step 9, incrementally migrate the legacy applications by rewriting the legacy modules to run directly against the target DBMS. Decide which applications to migrate first on the basis of simplicity and cost/importance. In step 10, incrementally migrate the legacy interfaces in the same way as the applications. An IS gateway could be used to support the migration. Then, in step 11, cut over to the target all operations. Cutover can begin as soon as the database migration is complete. It continues as applications are transitioned and can be extended indefinitely.

It should be noted that the lack of structure in the legacy applications and database service may make it difficult to determine if a legacy component can be isolated and retired after the corresponding target component has been cut over. Even if this is the goal of the effort, contingency plans should be made in case component retirement is either delayed or impossible.

4.3 CLOSING REMARKS

As we noted at the outset of this book, the general migration model is tailorable to varying types of legacy ISs, including those that exhibit closer and less desirable coupling between applications and database services. In this chapter, we've looked at a variation of the basic model that is useful for semidecomposable ISs. Essentially, we have only pointed out those steps that involve greater challenges than their counterparts in the decomposable migration strategy. In the next chapter, we'll see this migration strategy in action in the context of a case study.

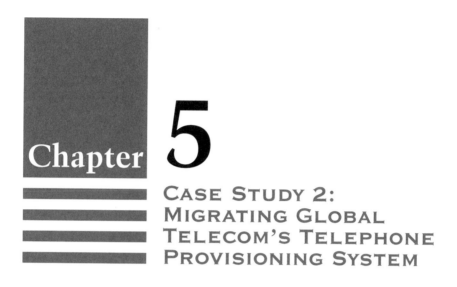

Chapter 5

CASE STUDY 2: MIGRATING GLOBAL TELECOM'S TELEPHONE PROVISIONING SYSTEM

*O**ne of us (Michael Brodie) participated in developing a migration plan for the telephone provisioning system (TPS) for a large telecommunications company. For convenience, we'll call this company "Global Telecom." This was an opportunity to apply the migration method for semidecomposable legacy ISs and extend it for the nondecomposable case. This chapter describes the semidecomposable legacy IS, TPS, and the proposed migration plan. Later, in Chapter 7, we return to this case study.*

5.1 SOME BASIC INFORMATION

TPS supports aspects of *telephone provisioning*. Telephone provisioning is the allocation and deployment of telephony resources to provide a customer with a requested telephone service.

Assume that a customer has called Global Telecom to request telephone service. Global Telecom must perform the following tasks:

- Verify the street address.

- Identify an available telephone number and the required telecommunications equipment from the available inventory. Equipment needed could include cable-pairs, line equipment, jumper wires, special circuits for advanced services, and a cross connect box.

- Assign the identified equipment inventory to the customer, remove them from the available inventory, and deploy them—for example, make the necessary connections and update the telephone switch that will serve the customer.

- Ensure that it works.

- Inaugurate the service.

Many other related functions are initiated directly or indirectly by TPS, including customer credit validation, account and billing setup, and directory services update. Ideally, service provisioning is completed during the initial customer contact.

This process is required for any change to a customer's telephone service. It is invoked over 100,000 times per day for the current customer base of 20,000,000. If one process fails, a customer may lose the requested telephone service. If many processes fail or if TPS goes down, large numbers of customers can be affected within minutes. Other types of failure can be costly. If inventory or assignments are not performed correctly, equipment may be kept out of service or may be inconsistently assigned, resulting in poor service or no service at all. If billing is not initiated correctly, the company may not be able to bill for delivered services or may bill for services not rendered. TPS is clearly mission-critical to Global Telecom.

TPS supports four basic functional areas.

Core functions: The core TPS functions are cable-pair assignment, inventory management, wire frame management, switch changes, network planning, central office conversion support, repair support, performance audits, and related reporting and auditing.

Street address guide (SAG): SAG manages all valid addresses, records services provided at each address, validates customer addresses, and identifies location for equipment assignment.

Dial office administration (DOA): This area of TPS assigns resources that optimally meet the customer and company requirements. DOA functions include assignment of telephone numbers and line equipment; load balancing of switching and line equipment; management of equipment reservations and availabilities, aging telephone numbers (you wouldn't want the telephone number that the local pizza parlor just gave up), and equipment rotation; and related reporting and administration.

Outside plant management (OSP): OSP manages and assigns telecommunications equipment, such as serving terminals and cross connect boxes, that is not inside a central office.

TPS's primary resource is the data it uses to run and administer telephone provisioning. This underscores a point we've made throughout this book: the fundamental value of legacy ISs—and the key to their migration—is buried in their data and not in their functions or code. (However, we do not mean to overlook data semantics buried in code, as with IMS applications. IMS databases embed lots of application semantics in their navigation paths that are embedded in the database and in the corresponding database calls.) Over 40 major ISs require information from, and actions to be performed by, TPS. For example, service order entry systems are the source of most telephone provisioning requests to TPS. Other major ISs requiring on-line access to TPS include systems for equipment testing, billing, verification, analysis, reporting, troubleshooting, repair support, telecommunication network management, and equipment ordering. Over 1,200 small systems (e.g., report writers) also require access to TPS's data. Hence, a fifth functional area is the provision of interfaces to many other ISs.

> The fundamental value of a legacy IS is buried in its data, not in its functions or code.

TPS is currently just under a million lines of FORTRAN code running on a Honeywell mainframe under a proprietary operating system. Its implementation consists of a massive program library—6,000 source code files, 1,500 executable modules—and an immense database of over a million data files of 900 file types, totaling approximately 400 gigabytes of data. TPS's transaction rate (100,000 per day) grows significantly during special operations like central office conversions. Data volumes, processing, and accesses grow at 20% per year. The scale of this problem should immediately convince you that Cold Turkey migration is entirely infeasible. Considering the functions it was designed to perform, TPS has run remarkably well and reliably, 24 hours a day, for 20 years with high user satisfaction. This operational reliability is one of its best features. As with most such legacy ISs, there are several development versions and several operational versions, which are in part the result of regulatory differences in deployment regions. This complicates the migration since the versions must all be maintained and modified.

The history and problems of TPS are typical of large legacy ISs. TPS began its life in 1972 as a small IS for managing the data used for installation and dispatch administration (e.g., installation and repair support) and switching services (e.g., switch changes, wire frame management). At that time, TPS was ideal for managing data for the then-current telephony technology and business processes and rules. As related business evolved, TPS was extended or altered to support these unanticipated, mission-critical changes. Hence, there was seldom a global plan with which to control the evolution or against which to develop a comprehensive, integrated design. Over its 20-year history, it grew by a few large extensions and a vast number of enhancements, modifications, and fixes.

TPS's inflexible and complex structure reflects this history. Applications are neither modular nor cleanly separable. Files, data structures, and indexes are convoluted, complex, and poorly structured. Programs and data are highly interdependent and redundant. This makes TPS hard to modify and renders some applications and data outdated or irrelevant, yet indispensable because of the little-understood dependencies.

Under current conditions, it is difficult to allocate resources or time to fix known problems (e.g., pointer chain failures that cause crashes and are costly to fix), let alone to make changes necessary to meet some current and future requirements. To complicate matters, other ISs have been built to augment TPS and thus avoid modifying TPS. However, these ISs require interactions with TPS.

The above concerns for this mission-critical system motivated over 25 studies to replace TPS. The failures of each of these studies to develop a feasible plan, and the failure of at least one Cold Turkey effort, led Global Telecom to request the study described here.

Let's look at an analysis of TPS, consider potential problems in the migration plan, and, where possible, propose means of reducing the problems.

5.2 ANALYSIS OF TPS

Analysis is complicated since *there is no complete specification or documentation*. There never is! What documentation exists is outdated, since changes have been and still are made so rapidly and so often to TPS that the requirements, specification, and documentation have not been kept current. The system itself is the only complete description.

As with the CMS case study (Chapter 3), it was previously believed that TPS would be hard, if not impossible, to decompose. The legacy TPS architecture is illustrated in Figure 5.1. Our analysis suggested that it could be decomposed into 11 logical components. There are four major functional components (core TPS, SAG, DOA, and OSP) and two minor functional components (advanced services administration and validation). The three interface components for major ISs are service order entry (SOE), interface application (IA), and switch interface (SI).

TPS ABBREVIATIONS	
SAG	street address guide
DOA	dial office administration
OSP	outside plant management
SOE	service order entry
IA	interface application
SI	switch interface

Also, TPS has one interface component for minor systems (access interface), utilities (not illustrated), and a database services component that manages TPS data.

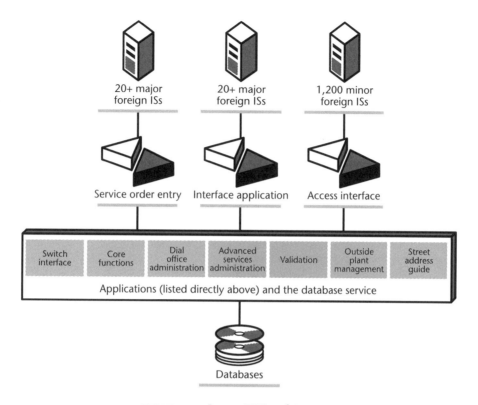

FIGURE 5.1 Legacy TPS architecture.

We also found that the TPS data could be decomposed into seven logical databases: one each for SAG, OSP, telephone numbers, pending orders, cable-pairs, wire frames, and inventory such as line equipment and miscellaneous supplies. A large number of files were found to be artifacts of the implementation—for example, indexes, output files, and administrative files. These need not be replicated in the target IS.

TPS's critical resource is the data, not the functionality. Hence, the primary goal of the TPS migration was determined to be data liberation. The TPS data should be migrated to a modern DBMS that can be accessed by other ISs. The target database must be designed to meet the current and known future requirements and be flexible enough to facilitate change. The lack of knowledge of the current data structures was not considered a major database design problem, since the database would not be duplicated. Rather, its logical requirements would be met. The logical requirements could be derived from code, actual data, functions, current and planned operation, and TPS experts. Since many known problems, including redundancy, are artifacts of the legacy design and implementation, they can be ignored when designing the target database, which will be correspondingly smaller with redundancies removed. It is also the case that the new business practices are more focused and simple, thus requiring less data than needed by the legacy business processes being replaced. A wisely chosen distributed target DBMS could meet all known requirements, including those for performance.

The major database challenges concern legacy database analysis, database cutover, data migration, and copy consistency. As stated above, there is little documentation of this massive database. Database cutover is a challenge because of the sheer volume of TPS data and the requirement for nonstop operation. Migrating TPS data to the target database is complicated by the lack of knowledge of the data structures and the limitations of TPS's database services. Following the Chicken Little strategy, we felt that the solution involved partitioning TPS data into small enough chunks for separate migrations and appropriately sequencing the migrations. The strategy we chose was to migrate the database in logical units centered around geographical regions. We would migrate one region at a time. Once the geographical region was selected, sequencing would be decided on the basis of which functions and data needed to be cut over in order to support the migration for that region.

Copy consistency requires that updates to TPS data be reflected in the corresponding copy in the target database. Defining the corresponding correctness criteria for coordinating updates is difficult and only part of the problem of establishing a mapping between the two databases. Supporting the required distributed transactions in the gateway further complicates the situation, requiring expert database systems skills. These difficulties could be significantly reduced by building the gateway using a distributed relational DBMS.

Continuing our analysis, we found that a significant amount of TPS interface code was redundant or obsolete and need not be migrated. The IS and user interfaces were redundant and in need of major improvements. We recommended that all user interfaces be migrated from the current linear screen technology to PC-based GUIs. The user interfaces significantly affect many clerks. The IS interfaces significantly affect over 40 existing mission-critical ISs and possibly many future ISs. Management was rightly concerned about both of these aspects. Hence, the benefits of interface improvements were used to sell the interface migration to management. Two benefits were interface standardization and the "single point of contact" policy intended to allow clerks to access any information that might be required during the customer contact session. These were excellent corporate policies that derived in part from the corporate business process reengineering activities.

> As with the Money Central migration, we knew it was to our advantage to radically reduce.

As with the CMS migration discussed in Chapter 3, the user interfaces can be rewritten efficiently using the 4GL of a relational DBMS. Because of the size of the interface migration, we recommended using standard user interface development environments and tool kits (e.g., Windows, X, Motif, Open Look).

In analysis we also found that the scope of application migration was smaller than anticipated. Many TPS functions were found to be redundant, obsolete, and inefficient, or would soon be so thanks to modern self-provisioning telephony equipment. Hence, many applications need not be migrated at all. Those that should be migrated should be correspondingly modified and simplified. As with the CMS migration, we reduced the application migration problem by focusing on only those functions that had to be migrated. We also planned no code migration whatever, thus simplifying the migration effort.

We did not have a good picture of the TPS workload or of what functions and data were most frequently accessed. We recommended that TPS be instrumented to capture this information as an aid in designing the target TPS.

5.3 THE TPS MIGRATION GATEWAY

We considered the TPS migration gateway to be the greatest technical challenge. As discussed in Chapter 4, such a gateway is hard to design, modify, and maintain throughout the migration. TPS's performance and interface requirements potentially add significantly to the challenge. We found the following ways to reduce the problem.

First, up to 80% of all TPS accesses are read-only. When data has been moved to the target DBMS, all read-only access can be directed there. This will improve performance, simplify the gateway, and reduce the load on TPS. The copy consistency problem is reduced since not all TPS functions and data will be migrated.

Also, since only 20% of TPS accesses involve updates, function migration and cutover chunks should be selected for migration and the migrations sequenced to further reduce the copy consistency problem. Because of TPS's complex structure, it is hard to determine when a migrated function can be isolated and retired, since live TPS functions may still depend on it.

In some cases, we planned to keep legacy data in the legacy repository and place all new data in the target; in others, the data was not time-critical. In these situations, we found that the target database need not be kept consistent with the legacy data. Hence, no update consistency or a less strict form of consistency was often possible, reducing the strict update consistency problem. Also, as data migrates to the target database and as access to legacy data decreases, the performance of the composite IS rises significantly, since more and more query and update traffic will be handled by the target DBMS, without translation.

Migrating the database early in the process permits benefits discussed above and provides a base for advanced provisioning functions not feasible under TPS. This would mean related new revenues for the services that could not be provisioned using TPS—a good point to emphasize to management when trying to sell the concept of early database migration. Hence, we recommended that the database migration be accelerated. Function migration should be planned and sold to management on the basis of meeting current business function requirements, reducing TPS's running and maintenance costs, and simplifying the gateway.

Most problems identified in the analysis could be reduced by selecting appropriately sized chunks to migrate and an appropriate sequence for the migrations and cutovers. Initially, chunks should be very small and independent. When the TPS migration is well underway and the risks and solutions are better understood, larger chunks may be reasonable.

The seven logical data chunks and corresponding functions, mentioned in Section 5.2, were too big for single migration steps given the operational requirements—migration time exceeds available downtime. Smaller chunks had to be found. The telephone network is supported by over 4,500 central offices, each of which contains one or more telephone switches. They are natural units of migration in the telephone business. Each can be treated independently. Central offices are the traditional units of conversion when upgrading the telephone network (e.g., upgrade or convert switches). Indeed, TPS itself is designed to facilitate central office conversion. We proposed a sequence of migrations based on chunks of TPS functionality, starting with SAG and portions of TPS data for one central office. Once a function or data chunk is migrated for one central office, the cutover can begin in more central offices.

These simplifications or details concerning a specific migration should emphasize to you that all migrations, like the legacy ISs being migrated here, are highly case-specific. You seldom face the worst imaginable problems. And when you do, you can take advantage of the specifics of a given legacy IS—its data, functions, structure, and use—to make the migration feasible, even when it seems, at first glance, impossible. Indeed, the TPS migration seemed impossible over the decade that more than 25 migration efforts were successively considered and then abandoned.

5.4 THE TPS MIGRATION PLAN, PART I

Because of the mission-critical role of TPS and its history of unsuccessful migration, TPS management wanted to see a plan for the first few steps of the proposed migration as a basis to study and verify the method. We estimated that it could take up to eight years to complete a full TPS migration. During an eight-year migration a detailed plan developed at the outset for the entire migration would become obsolete. Therefore, it made sense to us too that these first migrations be considered pilot studies or experiments to better understand the problems, technologies, and skill requirements as a basis for subsequent migrations.

We found that three portions of TPS—SAG, OSP, and the switch interface—were relatively easy to separate, migrate, and retire after migration. They are the focus of the first three migrations. Each migration is planned to follow the method for semidecomposable ISs.

TPS portions other than SAG, OSP, and the switch interface are less separable. They are more

> **THE PLAN, PART I**
>
> 1. Migrate the street address guide.
> 2. Migrate the outside plant.
> 3. Migrate the switch interface.
> 4. Migrate the TPS interfaces.

complex to migrate and cut over. It may not be possible to retire the remaining legacy portions once the target portion is cut over, since dependencies between the various legacy portions may still prevent this. Accordingly, the gateway must be designed to coordinate updates between legacy portions and their target counterparts. All nonupdate accesses can go to the target portions. Since portions of TPS may be important enough to keep but not important enough, or too complex, to migrate, those legacy portions may remain in the ultimate TPS. The corresponding gateway functions may also be required.

Migration 1: Migrate the street address guide.

We proposed for the first migration and pilot study that the SAG database and its associated functionality and interfaces be migrated. This was because SAG is the most easily separable portion and because SAG is required in the target TPS. The SAG migration could proceed as follows. Decompose TPS by separating the SAG application module from the other application modules and the SAG data from the legacy data. Create and install the TPS application gateway to deal only with SAG calls. Migrate the SAG interfaces, application, and database. We recommended that the migration and cutover be done incrementally, in iterations of one or more central offices, involving less than 100 megabytes of data. If successful, the incremental cutover could proceed with increasingly larger numbers of central offices until all 4,500 have been migrated. Once SAG is cut over, retire the legacy SAG application and data from legacy TPS.

Figure 5.2 illustrates the resulting TPS migration architecture. It includes TPS, as illustrated in Figure 5.1, and a decomposable target IS. The TPS application gateway manages all user and IS accesses since it encapsulates the legacy and target versions of TPS. The database component of the gateway will grow and shrink as the legacy database is incrementally migrated to the target DBMS and the composite IS evolves. We recommended a distributed DBMS because of target IS distribution requirements.

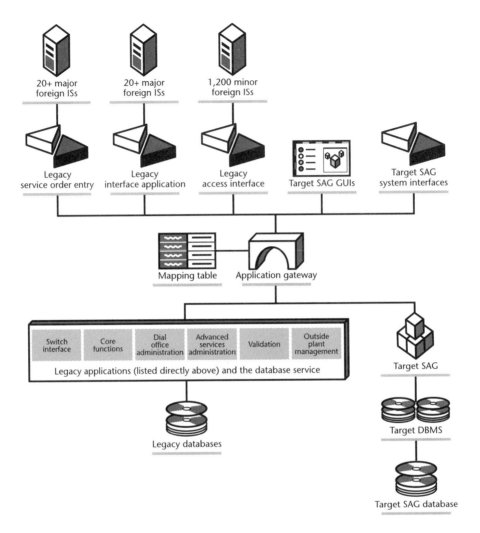

FIGURE 5.2 TPS after migration 1.

Migration 2: Migrate the outside plant.

We proposed OSP for the second migration step, since it was the next easiest to separate. However, the SAG and OSP migrations could proceed in parallel since they are so similar. The OSP migration is as follows. Separate the legacy OSP application module and data from TPS, as illustrated in Figure 5.3. Augment the TPS application gateway to handle OSP calls as well as SAG calls. Migrate the OSP interfaces, application, and database. We recommended an incremental cutover, again focused on central offices. Once OSP is cut over, retire the legacy OSP application and data from legacy TPS.

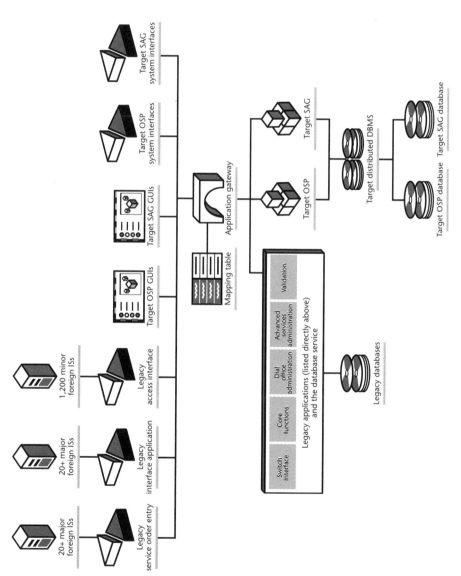

FIGURE 5.3 TPS after migration 2.

Migration 3: Migrate the TPS switch interface.

For many of the reasons cited above, we recommended TPS switch interface for the third migration. The migration of the TPS switch interface is very similar to the OSP migration, described above in migration 2. The legacy TPS switch interface component must be modified or cleaned up to be separated from the rest of TPS. Similarly, the corresponding data must be separated from the remaining TPS data. Both of these tasks were anticipated to be hard, indeed, harder than for SAG and OSP. This may be because the TPS switch interface was built earlier than SAG and OSP. The gateway must be augmented to deal with the future existence of a legacy and target copy of the switch interface function and data. Then the target switch interface database and function must be designed and installed in the architecture.

Data must be migrated incrementally from the legacy to the target, updating the mapping tables and gateway to ensure that calls to the switch interface are directed to the appropriate copy. Again, once the switch interface is entirely migrated, the legacy components can be eliminated. However, we cannot be sure that the rest of TPS does not depend on either the legacy switch interface function or data. The initial analysis and separation steps may help to establish this. However, since we do not know the structure and dependencies in TPS, we cannot be certain. So we must experiment to ensure that the legacy switch interface function and data can be eliminated. This extends to the function of the gateway also. If the rest of TPS is dependent on either legacy component, then the gateway must continue to direct update requests to the legacy components so that they are up-to-date. Once all legacy data and function is migrated to the target, all queries and updates can be directed to the target. The resulting architecture is illustrated in Figure 5.4.

Migration 4: Migrate the TPS interfaces.

The TPS interface migration is a large, complex process. It is mission-critical since all interfaces must remain operational throughout the migration. This includes interfaces for over 1,200 minor ISs and 40 major ISs. Unfortunately, the TPS interface migration is complicated by a second factor. Further analysis revealed that the applications yet to be migrated were not decomposable, as were some of their user and system interfaces. To simplify the migration, we proposed that the nonseparable interfaces be eliminated by altering the legacy applications to use one of the separable TPS interfaces (i.e., SOE, IA, access interface). We viewed this as necessary, even though it violated our goal of altering legacy code as little as possible. As a result, a large number of legacy user and system interfaces will have to be migrated.

We proposed that the TPS interface migration be accomplished using an IS gateway, illustrated in Figure 5.5. The TPS IS gateway provides the appearance to all existing ISs and end users that they continue to access the same

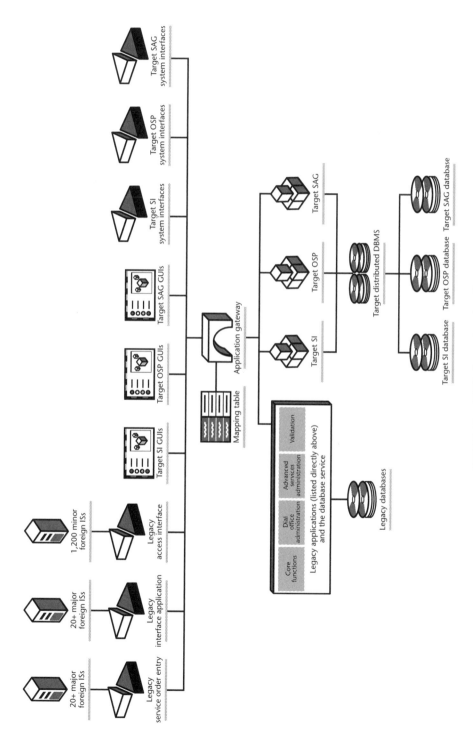

FIGURE 5.4 TPS after migration 3.

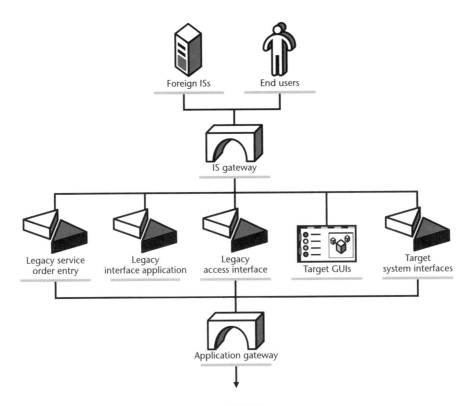

FIGURE 5.5 TPS IS gateway.

interfaces. However, the gateway can redirect the calls and the results appropriately to the current state of the migration. Global Telecom decided to use the IS gateway to introduce corporate interface standards and temporary versions of critical features that would not otherwise be in place until much later. Under cover of the TPS IS gateway, the legacy IS interfaces (SOE, IA, and access interface) must be migrated to the appropriate target IS interfaces. We recommended the development of one uniform IS interface to replace all three legacy IS interfaces.

Although TPS was believed to be semidecomposable, it was found to be hybrid, as illustrated in Figure 1.4. That is, after migration 4, we found that the remaining applications were nondecomposable, unless significant changes were made to the legacy IS that were deemed far too risky. Hence, migration 4 ended the semidecomposable migration. The remainder of TPS required a migration method for nondecomposable ISs, as described in Chapter 6. In Chapter 7 we continue the saga of TPS's migration with part II of the migration plan.

5.5 TPS MIGRATION HISTORY

Because of the size, significance, impact, and cost of TPS and the planned migration effort, its history is somewhat complex. It took five years to get started, to allocate the needed resources, and to convince the Global Telecom management that the plan was necessary and workable. But migration did begin, and it has been well under way for several years. Management, being appropriately cautious, developed several separate proof-of-concept tasks to investigate the plan. Because of the mission-critical nature of the TPS data and the relatively lesser importance of the code, significant efforts were mounted to achieve TPS data liberation.

The proposed street address guide migration was initiated. That SAG database alone is so large that it is being migrated incrementally. The success of this and related migration steps spurred the development of a general data liberation plan, including a data server strategy to design corporate data servers, into which all significant legacy data will be transitioned by techniques consistent with Chicken Little. It also includes a data migration engine, a hardware and software platform that is incrementally implementing the very challenging gateways and coordinators. A pilot version of the data migration engine is now in production. The data server strategy is in design, development and deployment. A separate activity was initiated to migrate TPS to a new computing environment in support of further migration steps.

Application and interface migrations were begun as separate activities. Interface migration was handled in coordination with a larger corporate effort to support "single point of contact," which provides a single user interface to all ISs to which agents need access during the course of a single customer contact session. Applications were migrated in conjunction with business process reengineering activities.

After the TPS migration started, a corporate business process reengineering activity began and became the driving force for all IS activities. Consistent with the Chicken Little principle of separately migrating different components of a legacy IS, several parallel migration activities are now underway in the areas of environment, data, interfaces, and applications.

In the area of computing environments, Global Telecom developed the future computing architecture for the entire telephone company (see Figure 8.6). It will be a distributed computing architecture similar to that being proposed by the Object Management Group (see Figure 8.1). A significant consideration in designing the architecture was to accommodate all legacy information systems (the vast majority of the operational base) as well as new ISs to be developed with advanced information technology such as object orientation. Another consideration was the migration requirements of legacy

ISs such as TPS. The future "applications architecture" was designed to facilitate these migrations and is consistent with the Chicken Little migration architectures.

In the data area, the data server and data migration engine activities were slowed during the development of the long-term architecture. Then they were restarted with increased vigor and direction, in cooperation with other migration and development efforts (see Figure 8.7). These activities were reoriented to meet the requirements of the more comprehensive business process reengineering plans. Interestingly enough, the data migrations were found to be very much in support of the reengineering goals, not only in plan but in technology and content. The plans made for the migration of a single legacy IS still held in the much broader context of migrating many legacy ISs. The data server migrations include both the SAG and the OSP migrations planned above. In the case of TPS, the data and environment migrations are proceeding separately from the applications and interface migrations.

The TPS legacy application and interface migrations were halted because of the process reengineering activities. Their future is less certain as the broader business process reengineering activities are worked out. Again, they were found to support business process reengineering in goals and technology. However, they were not supportive of the business processes in content. This reflects the view that legacy data is often mission-critical long after the corresponding legacy applications are no longer of use. Data may be shared across a much wider spectrum of applications, and thereby it is more global than individual applications and their interfaces.

Chapter 6

MIGRATING NONDECOMPOSABLE LEGACY ISs

As we noted in Chapter 1, the Chicken Little migration method is tailorable to different types of IS structures, including those that are nondecomposable—the most difficult kind to migrate or, for that matter, maintain. Nondecomposable migration architectures require an IS gateway, which encapsulates the entire IS. This gateway is difficult to build, but it plays a key role in the nondecomposable migration process.

In this chapter, we explore how the Chicken Little migration steps apply to nondecomposable legacy ISs, focusing our discussion on those aspects that vary from either decomposable or semidecomposable structures.

6.1 THE MIGRATION METHOD

Old ISs are commonly nondecomposable ISs. By old, we mean those built in the 1950s and 1960s, many built in the 1970s and 1980s, and even a few built in the 1990s. They provide little or no separation among what is now called user interface, database, and application code.

Many of these ISs were built before DBMS products existed. Data management was often provided through the application code, each time an application was built. In these cases, there is almost no separation between data management functions and application code. User interface functions were coded directly in the code when user interaction was required. Also, the concept of structuring applications into separate modules for different functions didn't even exist. These nonseparable architectures are obviously the most difficult to migrate.

The specially tailored Chicken Little steps for migrating nondecomposable ISs are listed below.

The Chicken Little Steps

1. Incrementally analyze the legacy IS.
2. Incrementally decompose the legacy IS structure.
3. Incrementally design the target interfaces.
4. Incrementally design the target applications.
5. Incrementally design the target database.
6. Incrementally install the target environment.
7. Incrementally create and install the IS gateway.
8. Incrementally migrate the legacy database.
9. Incrementally migrate the legacy applications.
10. Incrementally migrate the legacy interfaces.
11. Incrementally cut over to the target IS.

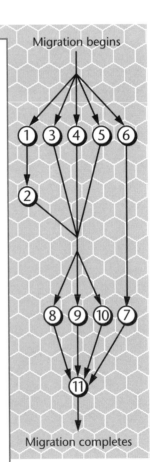

In the accompanying flowchart, note that some steps can proceed in parallel. You can start with analyzing the legacy IS (step 1), designing the target IS (any of steps 3, 4, or 5), or installing the target environment (step 6). You can decompose the legacy IS (step 2) after you've completed step 1. To install the gateway (step 7), you must have already installed the target environment (step 6). You can migrate the interfaces, applications, or database (steps 8, 9, 10), or install the gateway (step 7), in any order. When you have completed those steps, you are ready to cut over the IS (step 11). The above description is not for the entire IS, since that would be a Cold Turkey migration. The flow of steps is for each increment to be migrated, so the entire flow is repeated for each such increment.

It should be noted that some steps need not be done for each increment. Similarly, if the increment is of adequate size, it can be skipped entirely until another increment is required to support other increments. Figure 6.1 illustrates the migration architecture for nondecomposable legacy ISs.

In the following paragraphs, our discussions are brief in cases where the steps are the same as ones described for the decomposable and semidecomposable IS migration methods. Please see Sections 2.2 and 4.2 if you're looking for additional information.

Step 1: Incrementally Analyze the Legacy IS

This step can be arbitrarily complex. The legacy IS functions and data content must be analyzed from whatever information is available. Learn as much as you need from possible resources:

- documentation

- users, developers, maintainers, managers

- system dumps

- the history of its operation

- services known to be provided

It may be useful to conduct experiments to probe the system using the known interfaces and available tools.

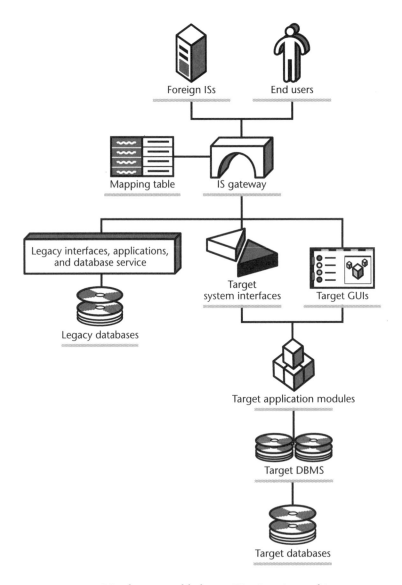

FIGURE 6.1 Nondecomposable legacy IS migration architecture.

The lack of structure may mean that the requirements must be defined from scratch; that is, distinct applications or functions may not be clear. When appropriately small chunks of data or functions can be identified but not proved to be independent, they may simply have to be replicated. The legacy and target copies must then be coordinated until it is demonstrably safe to retire the legacy versions.

In all cases, the level of detail required for the legacy IS migration should be driven by demand. That is, analyze the legacy IS to the extent that the information will serve the migration. We believe that in most cases a significant amount of the legacy data will not be migrated and almost none of the code. However, even if they are not migrated, it might be necessary to understand them to assist in migrating other related or dependent legacy components.

Step 2: Incrementally Decompose the Legacy IS Structure

The terms decomposable, semidecomposable, and nondecomposable refer to the general nature of the IS. The categorization does not mean to say that every component so classified strictly follows the category. Hence, it is useful to investigate the IS for any opportunities of which you can take advantage. If any decomposition can be achieved, the migration is simplified. If, on the other hand, you cannot decompose any components, you might be able to clean the IS up before migration (e.g., by making the boundaries clearer, etc.). Any restructuring can facilitate the migration.

Step 3: Incrementally Design the Target Interfaces

Designing and specifying the target interfaces first requires designing the software architecture of the target IS. The target GUIs, system interfaces, and an interface migration strategy also should be planned at this point.

Step 4: Incrementally Design the Target Applications

Design and specify the target applications. The applications that will run on the target platforms must be designed in accordance with the business processes and rules that will be supported in the target environment. On the basis of your assessment of the migration and the risk involved, decide whether the applications will be reengineered from those of the legacy environment or will closely match them.

Step 5: Incrementally Design the Target Database

Design a relational database schema to meet the data requirements of the target IS. We recommend that you first conduct a conventional DBMS evaluation. Use the results and those of the previous steps to help you reach an understanding of the target and legacy ISs. Then, proceed with the database design. Bear in mind that the complexity of this step may be large enough to warrant iterating in small increments.

Step 6: Incrementally Install the Target Environment

In Sections 2.2 and 4.2 we discussed the process of incrementally installing the target IS environment. The issues in this area don't vary from one legacy IS structure to another, as the target environment should be as modern as possible, regardless of the source environment. Use the most up-to-date architecture, products, and standards.

Step 7: Incrementally Create and Install the IS Gateway

An IS gateway encapsulates an *entire* IS, as opposed to a database gateway, which encapsulates only the database service, or an applications gateway, which encapsulates only the applications and the database service. This IS gateway is illustrated in Figure 1.6 and Figure 6.1. As described in Section 1.8, an IS gateway provides several functions. It captures all requests from users and provides the results of those requests back to the users. To do this, the IS gateway must deal with user interface issues (e.g., assist in migrating a legacy IS to a target IS) as well as invocation and coordination of appropriate legacy and target components. This makes the IS gateway very challenging to build. It could also include a *communications gateway* required to migrate from one communications technology or infrastructure to another (e.g., IBM's CICS to TCP/IP), thereby assisting the migration from mainframe to client/server architectures.

In previous methods, the gateway functionality decreases as legacy IS components are retired. Because of the lack of structure in the nondecomposable legacy IS, it may not be possible to retire any legacy components until the migration is complete. Hence, the IS gateway will continue to increase in complexity until the nondecomposable legacy IS can be retired.

In some cases, it may not be useful to migrate certain legacy IS components. For example, they may be required for seldom-accessed archival information or functions. Hence, the IS gateway may become an integral part of the ultimate IS.

Step 8: Incrementally Migrate the Legacy Database

The difficulty of this step depends on the results of the previous steps. It may be very difficult or costly to access data in legacy database services in nondecomposable legacy ISs. This could be because of the legacy database service, the applications, the structure of the data, or all of the above. It may be necessary to access legacy data solely through the application interfaces in order to avoid damaging the data. Indeed, in old systems, the applications provide access, query, update, and integrity functions. You may be forced to use these functions.

Step 9: Incrementally Migrate the Legacy Applications

Incrementally migrate the legacy applications by rewriting the legacy modules to run directly against the target DBMS. Decide which applications to migrate first on the basis of simplicity and cost/importance.

Step 10: Incrementally Migrate the Legacy Interfaces

Incrementally migrate the legacy interfaces in the same way as the applications. An IS gateway could be used to support the migration.

Step 11: Incrementally Cut Over to the Target IS

Cut over to the target all necessary operations. Cutover can begin as soon as the database migration is complete, or even after increments of the migration are complete. It continues as applications are transitioned and can be extended indefinitely.

6.2 CLOSING REMARKS

It's important to note that even though the lists of 11 migration steps seem to vary little from one legacy structure type to another, there are in fact differences that are directly related to the legacy environment type. Nondecomposable ISs require an IS gateway, semidecomposable ISs an application gateway, and decomposable ISs a database gateway.

It is imperative to get this right: make sure you match the proper gateway with the legacy IS structure. Mismatches will significantly increase the risk to the entire migration process. As illustrated in Figure 1.6, a typical large-scale IS that has evolved over many years may require each type of gateway.

> Make sure you match the proper gateway with your legacy IS structure.

In the next chapter, we resume our discussion of the TPS migration, specifically, the nondecomposable portion.

109

Chapter 7

MIGRATING LEGACY ISs: A GENERAL CASE

*I*n this chapter, we discuss the general case migration method for legacy ISs. This migration method is a combination of the previous migration methods. It's the most broadly applicable of those presented in this book; it applies to all legacy ISs, since each is a special case of the general case illustrated in Figure 1.4.

We also return to the discussion of Global Telecom's TPS. Here, we extend the TPS migration plan to handle its nondecomposable portion.

7.1 ARCHITECTURE NOTES

In earlier chapters we describe three major variations of the Chicken Little migration method. They are predicated on the assumption that the legacy IS to be migrated falls strictly into one architectural category. However, this assumption is seldom true. The longer the IS has been in existence, the more variations in its structure are likely. As mentioned in Section 1.6.4, many older legacy ISs are really a hybrid of the three architectures. The oldest parts may be nondecomposable, whereas new parts may be semidecomposable or even decomposable. Treating the legacy IS as nondecomposable because a portion of it falls into this category makes the migration much more complicated than it need be. If there are decomposable components, take advantage of them. Consequently, old legacy ISs that have aspects of all three architectures can be migrated by combining the three methods to arrive at what we call the general

111

case. The migration architecture for this general case is a combination of the migration architectures for the three legacy IS types, as shown in Figure 7.1.

The migration architecture must be tailored to the specific requirements of each unique legacy IS. A simple combination of the gateways, as illustrated in Figure 7.1, may not be appropriate. For example, it may not make sense to place some target application modules above the database gateway. Instead they may be more appropriately placed below the gateways to directly access the target DBMS. In this case, the corresponding GUIs would interact directly through the application gateway.

7.2 THE GENERAL CASE

The migration method for arbitrary legacy ISs is a combination of the migration methods for decomposable, semidecomposable, and nondecomposable legacy ISs. Our starting point is a hybrid legacy IS, as illustrated in Figure 1.4. Our target is a decomposable legacy IS, as illustrated in Figure 2.1.

The steps of the method are as follows:

The Chicken Little Steps

1. Incrementally analyze the legacy IS.
2. Incrementally decompose the legacy IS structure.
3. Incrementally design the target IS.
4. Incrementally install the target environment.
5. Incrementally migrate the portions identified in step 2.

To permit work to proceed in parallel, the steps of the method should be as independent as possible. You can begin with analyzing the legacy IS (step 1), designing the target IS (step 3), or installing the target environment (step 4). You can decompose the legacy IS (step 2) after you've completed step 1. To begin step 5, incremental migration of the various decomposed portions—decomposable, semidecomposable, and nondecomposable—you must have already analyzed the legacy IS, decomposed the legacy IS, designed the target IS, and installed the target environment (steps 1–4). The above flow of steps is for each increment to be migrated, so the entire flow is repeated for each such increment. Each step is discussed below.

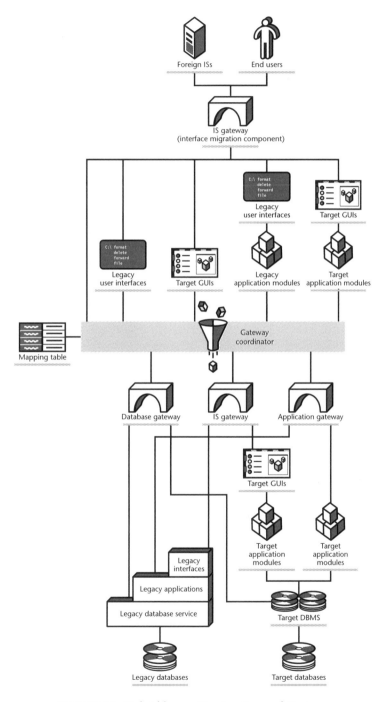

FIGURE 7.1 Hybrid legacy IS migration architecture.

Step 1: Incrementally Analyze the Legacy IS

Our goal here is to determine what portions of the legacy IS are decomposable, semidecomposable, and nondecomposable. Learn as much as you can about your IS by studying the available resources. Some extra effort and time spent on this step will considerably ease your progress through the rest of the migration.

Step 2: Incrementally Decompose the Legacy IS Structure

Once the analysis of the previous step is completed, as much decomposition as is reasonable should occur. The result will likely be a mix of decomposable, semidecomposable, and nondecomposable portions. Hopefully this mix will be weighted more toward the decomposable side of the spectrum. Consider altering the legacy IS to facilitate the migration and achieve the migration architecture illustrated in Figure 7.1.

Step 3: Incrementally Design the Target IS

Design the target IS architecture to meet target IS requirements. All target components must be designed to support target business requirements. Design and specify the target interfaces, database, and applications.

Step 4: Incrementally Install the Target Environment

Treat the target environment as if it were being developed from scratch, exclusive of the migration-oriented issues. Once you've selected your target environment, test it and then install it.

This step involves significant changes across the board. You'll have to make substantial investments in hardware and systems software. You'll have to rethink and restrategize the applications, development, and maintenance architectures. Moreover, users and management will need time to adjust to the new environment. See Section 2.2 for more discussion of this step.

Step 5: Incrementally Migrate

For each of the portions that result from step 2, the appropriate legacy IS migration method is applied. That is, the decomposable portions would be handled as discussed in Section 2.4, the semidecomposable portions would follow steps from Section 4.2, and the nondecomposable portions would be treated as discussed in Section 6.1. You will be using various types of gateways, depending on the migration methods being applied. See Table 7.1.

Migration portion	Gateway type
Decomposable	Database
Semidecomposable	Application
Nondecomposable	IS

TABLE 7.1 Gateways used with Chicken Little migration methods.

7.3 THE TPS MIGRATION PLAN, PART II

Now that we've introduced the general case method, we can continue the discussion of TPS that we began in Chapter 5. Note that, since we already designed the target IS in part I of the migration plan (Chapter 5), step 3 of the general method does not need to be represented in this discussion. We do, however, apply the rest of the steps of the general method to part II of the TPS migration plan.

Initial analysis determined that TPS could be decomposed into the following components:

- three separable applications (street address guide, outside plant, and switch interface)

- three separable IS interfaces (service order entry, interface application, and access interface)

- the rest of TPS

Further analysis found that a portion of the rest of TPS (the third component) was in fact semi-decomposable. We can apply the semidecomposable migration method from Section 4.2 to this portion (i.e., step 5 of the general method). The remainder was found to be nondecomposable.

Since the rest of TPS is nondecomposable, it is hard to analyze for functional boundaries and so on. However, analyzed from the outside, so to speak, we can determine the various functions performed even if we cannot distinguish the code or design boundaries between the components that implement them.

TPS was a particularly bad case of nondecomposable legacy database structure. First, there was almost no knowledge of the internal structure of the legacy database. This was complicated by the fact that the physical structure was cluttered with implementation artifacts that were hard to distinguish from application data. As a result, we proposed that the existing legacy applications (e.g., database query, report generation, and access routines) be used to extract legacy data. This significantly lengthened the database migration time because of the slow non-bulk processing time.

Again, since the rest of TPS is nondecomposable, presumably we can't do much in the way of decomposing (step 2 of the general method). Not so.

Legacy code is famous for mess, like an old, dilapidated house or building. We can clean up the legacy nondecomposable code in many ways. Indeed, a significant number of tools can assist with this activity. They are typically called reengineering tools, but they can be directed at cleaning up the consequences of long-term maintenance and evolution for the purpose of continued operations. (Recently, another type of reengineering tool has received attention: those for reimplementing ISs.) However, the cleanup type of reengineering tools may be very useful in the migration context since the cleanup of the legacy IS may ease the analysis and migration steps. Also, significant aspects of the legacy IS may not be migrated, in which case the cleanup improves it for the long haul.

Step 4 of the general method, as with all other environment installation steps throughout the book, requires an analysis of sizing and scaling of data and processing capabilities of the target IS. For the TPS migration, we recommended that machines and network configurations be selected to accommodate the data and function distribution as well as communication and computing requirements (e.g., performance-distributed operating systems, etc.).

Figure 7.2 illustrates the resulting TPS architecture.

7.4 CLOSING REMARKS

In this chapter, we generalized our discussion, focusing on the fact that Chicken Little is applicable to different legacy IS architectures. Note that the complexity shown in Figure 7.2 is typical of hybrid architectures, containing two or three different architectural constructs. Many different gateways are likely to be needed in such environments.

We recommend that you analyze your legacy IS to determine its structure and then select the Chicken Little method that is most appropriate, considering the available tools and the amount of work. For example, if a legacy IS is largely nondecomposable, developing a method and gateways to support a small decomposable component may not be reasonable. Ultimately, the method you choose should be determined by the architecture of the legacy IS and by the required migration architecture. As you saw in this chapter, a hybrid legacy IS and the corresponding general migration method and migration architecture are the most complex of all the choices, but at the potential savings of easier migration steps. Your choice may be determined by other factors entirely, such as available migration tools or environments, or the migration schedule set by business and other factors. Whatever you do, work out the entire plan and get the big picture before you make your decision.

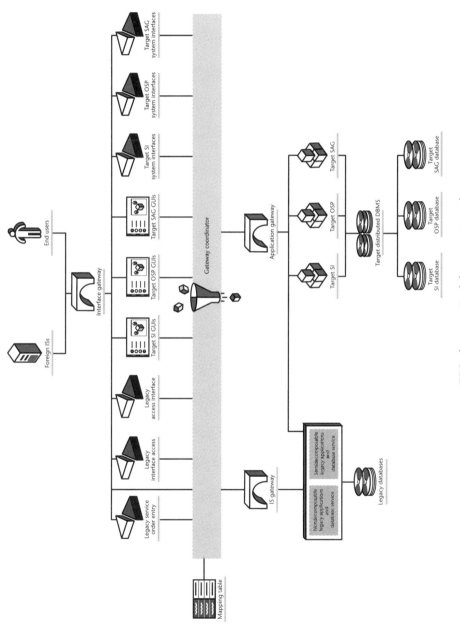

FIGURE 7.2 TPS after part II of the migration plan.

117

Chapter 8

DISTRIBUTED COMPUTING AND INCREMENTAL MIGRATION

W e have little doubt that the vast majority of future business ISs will be distributed and based, to some significant degree, on object-oriented computing. Consider client/server. It is seen as an economic necessity, to say nothing about the technical benefits of component-oriented, distributed computing or the benefits of object orientation. These benefits are largely ones of interoperability, portability, and flexibility. That is, distributed and object-oriented computing is our best shot at developing information systems that can evolve in response to changing business requirements and technology improvements. Consequently, we believe that future information systems will be distributed, object-oriented, to some degree component-oriented, and heterogeneous. By heterogeneous, we mean that they will be written in a variety of languages as well as portable from one environment to another and from one machine to another.

How does this view of the future relate to migrating those old legacy systems? In short, do as much as you can to ensure that the target information system will not resist change and become yet another legacy system. Your resulting information system, the target of the migration, should facilitate change resulting from business or technical requirements. It is our view that cooperative information *systems, those made up of cooperating components, possibly distributed over many client/server machines, are our best shot at evolvable (non-legacy) information systems. We hasten to note that robust, complete systems, languages, and methodologies do not yet exist to support such large-scale distributed systems. However, it is well underway, supported by almost all hardware and software vendors of significance. See Brodie's article (1992) or any IS trade publication for more details.*

Designing the wrong target architecture may place your organization in a worse position than it already is with the existing legacy system. Our premise is, design your architecture to be as consistent as is feasible with distributed object computing. The increments selected for the Chicken Little migration steps will very likely concern a component in the distributed information system, either part of the architecture or of the application function. It is no coincidence that the incremental nature of Chicken Little fits exactly with the component-oriented nature of distributed object computing, of which client/server was the vanguard.

In this chapter we describe several alternative and, in some cases, complementary technologies. They provide a base for the distributed computing architectures that can be used for migration and target architectures. We also briefly introduce distributed computing principles and architectures and then turn to a discussion of these architectures as a basis for legacy IS migration.

We focus on CORBA (Common Object Request Broker Architecture) to further discuss the distributed object computing approach, but we could just as easily have focused on OLE/COM (Object Linking and Embedding built on the Common Object Model) in our discussion. We discuss distributed database architectures and indicate why we believe they will overtake transaction monitors as a better approach to distributed data and distributed objects. In the long term, nothing will be purely one architecture or the other. What is most likely is that, in the long term, all enterprise computing architectures, what we have called target architectures, will be combined architectures.

The combination will depend on many things, including marketplace competition. However, there is one critical requirement of these architectures: they must support transparent interoperability between the architectures themselves. Considerable progress is being made in this area.

8.1 SUPPORTING TECHNOLOGIES

Alternative technologies that provide a base for distributed computing architectures include

- CORBA
- OLE/COM
- distributed databases (DDBMSs)
- transaction monitors
- combined data and distributed computing technologies

Distributed computing is new. The supporting technologies, such as those listed above, are all immature in various ways. CORBA and OLE/COM are being developed to support general-purpose distributed computing. Their current plans for supporting distributed data are via a distributed data management service that is not part of the core architecture but is supported through an attached service (e.g., transaction, persistence, and query service for CORBA; NILE for OLE/COM). DDBMSs support distributed data but not distributed computation. Transaction monitors support distributed transactions, but not general-purpose distributed computation or distributed data. A fifth alternative combines distributed data and distributed computing technologies to support both fully but separately.

All of these alternative technologies are evolving to more complete solutions that will be robust, flexible, and all those good things. Current products for each alternative are not completely satisfactory, each for different reasons. We recommend that you select your migration architecture to be as close to your desired target architecture as possible, making the appropriate compromises to meet your requirements, so that the subsequent migration to the desired target is facilitated. For example, you may feel that your requirements force you to select an architecture that is not what you might like to choose for your long-term vision (e.g., CORBA, because of the lack of maturity and robustness of available CORBA products). Instead, you may choose a distributed database architecture, which, although mature and robust with respect to some important data management requirements, is immature in others (e.g., distributed computing functionality). Later, as complete and robust CORBA products become available, you could migrate from a distributed database architecture to CORBA.

This plan is feasible because the distributed database architecture could be made interoperable with a CORBA architecture through one of the supporting technologies. However, it may be considerably more work to migrate the distributed database architecture and all the computing resources to a more

121

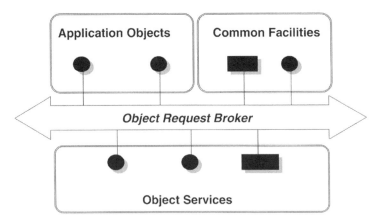

FIGURE 8.1 OMG Object Management Architecture.

CORBA-oriented architecture, one in which computation is distributed in the CORBA world while the data resides in the database world. This argument concerning the possible choice of an intermediate architecture applies, to different degrees and with different details, to every choice that you might make, since all alternatives are currently immature. Yet each provides an adequate basis to start today.

8.1.1 CORBA

The Object Management Group (OMG) is an industry consortium of over 500 hardware and software vendors as well as potential end-user organizations. Its charter is to develop and standardize specifications for the technology necessary to support general-purpose interoperability. To achieve this, OMG has specified a framework model called the Object Management Architecture (OMA), illustrated in Figure 8.1. The OMG approach to interoperability is to use object-oriented technology, but the objects in the resulting distributed computing environment need not be object-oriented. They can be legacy information systems encapsulated in an object-oriented interface. OMG's core architecture service, CORBA, supports object-to-object interoperability by permitting objects anywhere in the CORBA distributed computing environment to exchange messages. Interoperability between different Object Request Brokers (ORBs) has been specified, and its support in products is imminent. Such interoperability is supported for objects regardless of whether they are application objects or infrastructure objects such as what OMG calls common services (e.g., transaction service, query service, persistence) or common facilities (e.g., calendar facility). Hence, CORBA is a candidate for a target distributed computing architecture and the migration architecture. However, it does not directly support distributed data or distributed transactions. It would do so by means of what are termed object services (i.e., a DDBMS service and a transaction service) attached, via gateways, to the architecture.

CORBA is being supported by most of the world's significant hardware and software vendors. These vendors have been releasing CORBA products since 1991. CORBA is considered by many to be the future standard distributed computing architecture. However, at the present time, CORBA technology and supporting products are far from complete or robust for large-scale systems.

If you'd like further information about OMG and CORBA, OMG documents can be obtained by contacting your bookstore or the Object Management Group, Inc., Framingham Corporate Center, 492 Old Connecticut Path, Framingham, MA 01701-4568. You can also reach OMG by phone, (508) 820-4300, or electronically, info@omg.org or WWW: http://www.omg.org/

8.1.2 OLE/COM

Like CORBA, Microsoft's OLE/COM allows an interface to call an application without being aware of the application's internal implementation details. Currently, the application must reside on the same machine as the interface, but support for distribution is imminent. OLE/COM and CORBA could be viewed as competing approaches with similar goals. However, Microsoft and DEC have proposed an OMG specification for a CORBA/COM gateway to support interoperability between the two environments. Hence, although OLE/COM differs significantly in technical approach from CORBA, a CORBA/COM gateway is being standardized by OMG. This gateway will facilitate interoperability between applications in the two environments. Like CORBA, OLE/COM directly supports distributed computation but not distributed data or transactions. It supports distributed data and transactions through its strategy called NILE, which uses attached DBMS and transaction monitors.

Microsoft provides the operating system of choice for 90% of the world's desktops. Therefore Microsoft controls almost all desktops worldwide. This monopoly lends to their predisposition to "do their own thing." Because of the dominant position of Microsoft in the marketplace, as well as the ultimate functionality and robustness of Microsoft products, the OLE/COM alternative is a serious contender for future enterprise information architectures.

8.1.3 Distributed Databases

Relational DBMS products permit a client program to interact with remote databases in a distributed environment. Moreover, most RDBMS products support location transparency—the ability of a client to interact with data at remote sites without having to know where the data is. Systems with this capability are called distributed DBMSs. Moreover, DDBMS implementations are moving quickly to support distributed transactions, multiple copies of data objects, and parallel execution of user queries on the multiple machines in a distributed computing environment. Hence, DDBMSs provide a distributed computing architecture that supports access to distributed data. Moreover, through gateways, DDBMSs can support access to data stored in multiple heterogeneous DBMSs.

Because of the robustness and functionality of existing DDBMS products, we recommend their use to build some of the gateways described in previous chapters of this book. DDBMSs directly support distribution required by database gateways (i.e., data distribution) as opposed to distribution required by application and IS gateways (i.e., application distribution). However, DDBMS technology is rapidly being extended to support distributed objects (e.g., applications and interfaces as well as data). The main standard in this area is SQL-3, now being worked on by the ANSI X3H2 committee. Using SQL-3, methods and, indeed, whole applications will be directly supported by next-generation DBMSs. That is, next-generation DBMSs will support the storage and management of arbitrary objects whether they be what we currently consider data, applications, or interfaces. Hence, next-generation DBMS architectures could provide a complete solution for cooperative information systems. These next-generation DBMS architectures could support or manage the data, the applications, and the interfaces. In a DDBMS architecture, users will invoke methods through end-user interfaces (e.g., GUIs). In turn, GUIs invoke applications. Application invocation can be implemented using methods embedded in SQL queries or other next-generation languages. But for right now, DDBMSs support distributed data and transactions but not general-purpose distributed computation.

Because of the long-term track record of database technology as a core technology for all data-intensive applications, along with the planned extensions described above, SQL-3 DDBMSs may provide the basis of future distributed information systems. In other words, SQL-3 DDBMSs may provide the basis for the migration and target architectures being addressed in this chapter.

8.1.4 Transaction Monitors

For many years, transaction monitors have provided support for distributed applications. Historically, transaction monitors were designed to provide efficiency within large IBM mainframe environments. CICS (Customer Information and Control System) and IMS-DC (Information Management System-Data Communications) are two of the most popular early transaction monitors. Primarily, they supported efficient access from remote terminals to mainframe services, including databases.

With the arrival of workstations and PCs to replace dumb terminals, the role of transaction monitors has been extended. Specifically, a user interface running on a desktop can use a transaction monitor to access a variety of remote databases and services, usually with the ability to support distributed transactions among the services. As such, a transaction monitor can support distribution between a user interface and an application or a DBMS. Popular second-generation transaction monitors include Tuxedo from AT&T and Encina from IBM. Transaction monitors directly support distributed transactions but not distributed data or general-purpose distributed computation.

Transaction monitor vendors are proposing that they provide the target architecture for distributed information systems. Hence, transaction monitors would be candidates for the migration architecture. However, they would have to be extended and augmented with additional technology to support the functionality required in a distributed computing architecture.

8.1.5 Combined Architecture

The CORBA and OLE/COM architectures are intended to be general-purpose distributed object computing architectures. As such they would support any type of distributed, interoperable computation. However, they must be augmented with the infrastructure services necessary to support specific computational requirements. Obvious examples of powerful and necessary infrastructure or middleware services include a DDBMS service and a distributed transaction service. Hence, to support robust, reliable, efficient, and full-functioning data management and transactions, any CORBA or OLE/COM architecture must include the distributed database and transaction monitor technologies proposed above as alternatives. So they are not really alternatives; they are complementary technologies that, combined, provide a complete architecture for distributed computation, distributed data, and distributed transactions.

The four "alternative" technologies can be used in combination to provide a wide range of alternative distributed computing architectures that can serve as target and migration architectures. In Sections 8.2 and 8.4 we use CORBA to illustrate the distributed object computing architecture, but we could just as easily use OLE/COM. Similarly, in Section 8.3 we use DDBMSs and a powerful middleware service, whereas, with some restrictions, we could use transaction monitors. The distributed database architecture can be implemented in concert with a CORBA-based architecture. There are two extremes in this combination and a wide range of alternatives between. At one extreme, you can build an entire distributed database solution, as described above and in more detail below. Let's call it the maximal database architecture, and bridge it to a CORBA-based computing architecture, a distributed object environment. You would do this to provide access from new CORBA-based, distributed applications to the resources in the distributed database environment. At the other extreme, you can use a DDBMS to support just the target data management functions. Let's call this the minimal database architecture, and place all other computing components (e.g., interfaces, applications) in the CORBA architecture. Alternatives between the minimal and maximal database architecture vary depending on the number of non-data management components that are in the distributed database versus the distributed object environments. The minimal and maximal database architectures are both architectures for distributing everything; hence, they are complete solutions in their own right. However, the CORBA-based approach requires a data management service. If you choose the CORBA approach, we suggest that you follow the DDBMS approach, at least for data management.

In practice some end-user organizations may choose one or more of the above alternatives. Let's say they choose the pure distributed database architecture. We know from past experience that companies merge, get broken up, must interoperate with other companies, or develop multiple alternative strategies. In any case, it is highly likely that companies will have to interoperate across more than one of the above alternatives. In that case, they will encounter the combined approach. If vendors of any particular approach (e.g., OLE/COM) do not support interoperability with other architectures, they are not going to meet the requirements of their customers. We've seen that before. Indeed, it is, in part, why we face massive interoperability problems today. However, we see less and less of this vendor attitude as the end-user requirements for interoperability become a fundamental requirement of all future technologies and a dominant reality of the marketplace.

8.1.6 The Horse Race

There is now a horse race between the various technology alternatives. DDBMS vendors have already solved the problems of interoperability, hardware universality, and distributed transaction support. Now they are working on object support. CORBA provides support for distributed computation and, through attached services, support for distributed data and transactions. They are working on interoperability, hardware universality, and many other details of general-purpose distributed computing not being considered for DDBMSs. OLE/COM is comparable to CORBA in functionality and evolution, but it is a Microsoft proprietary solution. It's anybody's guess which technology will mature first. There are arguments that some or all of the above alternatives will not mature as planned, either for technical reasons or for nontechnical reasons such as dominance of a particular approach based on market share of the relevant products or on the earlier presence in the market of a complete, robust solution.

As we have already said, there will be a wide range of architectures that combine two or more of the alternatives. As a result, over time there will be at least four reasonable distribution architectures that support our legacy migration model. There may be more. Table 8.1 summarizes some differences between the alternatives.

Technology alternative	Maturity relative to requirements	Support distributed computing	Support data distribution	Likelihood of success
CORBA	Low	Yes	No	Medium
OLE/COM	Low/medium	Yes	No	Medium
Distributed databases	Medium	Database applications	Yes	Medium
Transaction monitors	Medium	Transactions	No	Low
Combined architecture	Low	Yes	Yes	High

TABLE 8.1 Comparison of technology alternatives.

Table 8.1 indicates that CORBA and OLE/COM are intended to provide a distributed computing architecture in which all computing resources are to be distributed. However, the basic CORBA and OLE/COM technology supports message and resource distribution. They do not support data distribution, per se, but they do provide an architecture in which such services can be supported. That is, a complete target or migration architecture based on CORBA or OLE/COM requires a distributed database service. A distributed database supports distributed data; indeed, it is the technology for this purpose. DDBMSs are being extended to support distributed processing but without the generality intended for CORBA and OLE/COM. Transaction monitors support distributed transaction processing via message passing. They are not intended to support distributed data or distributed processing other than distributed and reliable message passing for distributed transactions. Finally, the combined architecture will support distributed everything. CORBA or OLE/COM will support distributed processing, and the distributed database technology will support distributed data and the relevant distributed data processing, such as queries and transactions. This solution combines the best technologies for the two different requirements, data and processing.

However, in the combined architecture, the two technologies are not fully integrated. There are really two architectures and two worlds. Processing is distributed and supported by distributed computing technologies (e.g., CORBA, OLE/COM) and distributed data is supported by distributed database technology. Data and transaction distribution are supported in the distributed database technology and not in CORBA or OLE/COM, while general-purpose distributed processing is supported in CORBA and OLE/COM but not in the distributed database technology. To provide distributed queries or transactions over distributed objects, they must be under the control of a manager that supports queries and transactions, respectively, and for which there is a gateway provided by a CORBA or OLE/COM query or transaction service. DBMSs support distributed queries and transactions. Hence, building such a gateway, based on an IDL-to-SQL mapping, is relatively easy and is currently being done. It is a much harder task to build a query or transaction service for, say, distributed SmallTalk or any other object-oriented non-DBMS object manager, let alone the gateway to it.

Distributed, object-oriented queries and transactions are open research problems. These challenges force the two worlds to be separate for some time. Nonetheless, the combination of CORBA or OLE/COM distributed computation with the distributed data and transactions of a distributed database is not only powerful, it is a completely adequate solution for a corporate computing architecture, what we above called an enterprise information architecture, as well as for the target and migration architectures required for Chicken Little migrations.

8.2 DISTRIBUTED COMPUTING PRINCIPLES

At the simplest level, distributed computing involves the division of information processing and management responsibilities among multiple ISs that are connected via a message-passing communications mechanism. We can consider this connection at several successive levels:

> Connectivity and interoperability provide the technical base on which cooperative ISs are built.

- *Connectivity:* the ability of ISs to exchange messages with each other.

- *Interoperability:* ISs can not only exchange messages (i.e., support basic connectivity) but also request and receive services from each other. In effect, they can use each other's functionality. Interoperability requires the mutual understanding of the exchanged messages. That is, one IS can knowledgeably request the services of another and understand the responses.

- *Cooperation:* ISs execute tasks jointly. That is, two or more ISs use their mutual understanding to interoperate, achieving tasks that none of them could achieve alone.

Interoperability requires connectivity to send and receive messages. Centralized systems developed for one machine and in one language are trivially connected and interoperable. In a client/server environment, IS components may be distributed and even written in different languages. As distribution and heterogeneity increase, so do the challenges of connectivity and interoperation. In any case, connectivity and interoperability provide the technical base on which cooperative ISs are built. The higher-level task, the division of IS functionality among components, and the mutual "understanding" of interoperating components are all largely application-specific and not core technology issues.

Interoperation between components of an IS involve a technical component (e.g., how do they interact, such as in sending messages?) and a semantic component. From our case study in Chapters 5 and 7, migrating TPS involves establishing a mechanism (e.g., the architecture) to permit legacy and target components to communicate or interoperate, at the technical level. It also involves how they relate semantically, in terms of cooperating to perform the higher-level functions. The higher-level functions in TPS are telecommunications service provisioning. This involves many steps that customers need know nothing about, but TPS needs to know in detail since the provisioning is done only if all the steps are done.

Technical interoperability is a challenge that involves a technical solution. Semantic interoperability is a bigger challenge that requires a business solution (e.g., which functions or steps are required, and in what order?) and a corresponding technical solution so that the corresponding components can "understand" the request made of them in the context of the business process. For example, in TPS, the directory component needs to update its directory information to reflect that the person for whom the service is being provisioned now has that service. This is one of the final steps in the provisioning of that service.

In a very real sense, these ideas have been around and in use for many years. Many approaches to ISs focus on decomposing IS functions over modules. Then cooperation among the modules achieves the IS functions. Today more complexity is being added by considering modules to be physically distributed, autonomous (able to act independently of all other modules in the IS), and heterogeneous (written in different languages on different operating and communications systems). This leads us to the terminology that focuses on these major differences. This trend involves the use of component-oriented integration to achieve heterogeneous, autonomous, and distributed (HAD) systems.

The implications for Chicken Little incremental migration are conceptually simple, but as technically hard as achieving HAD systems. The legacy IS could be considered as a collection of modules. Meanwhile, the target IS should be designed as a cooperative IS that is potentially HAD to meet requirements. Then the migration proceeds as follows. One or more legacy IS modules acts as a migration increment while the target module is a component of the target cooperative IS. The key characteristics of target cooperative ISs and the architectures in which legacy migration to them occurs are

- object orientation
- open architecture
- standards-based language

8.2.1 Object Orientation

There is a growing trend toward object orientation within the IS community. Increasingly, ISs are being considered for object-oriented development. But less obviously and more significantly, products are developed using object-oriented technologies and methodologies. These products, those with which information systems are built, are establishing a strong object-oriented foundation for the future distributed-object computing environments.

On the basis of the claimed benefits of object orientation and the increasingly complex requirements of infrastructure technology, many infrastructure vendors are building their products using object-oriented technology. This implementation strategy may not be obvious to the IT shop that buys and deploys the resulting systems. Hence, object orientation is being introduced into organizations, worldwide, without an explicit strategy by IT shops to do so.

The applicability of the object-oriented paradigm to component integration is because of the intrinsic characteristics of object-oriented technology. Heterogeneity is supported because the messages passed among objects depend only on component interfaces, not on the internals of the objects themselves. Therefore, as long as the interfaces conform to protocols that are understandable by components that need to interoperate, the underlying subsystems may reside on various platforms (both legacy and target environment), be implemented in different manners (mainframe-based 3GL or assembler, target environment 4GL or visual programming system, etc.), and have other characteristics that are distinct from one implementation to another.

Additionally, an object-oriented approach supports autonomy, or the ability of locally defined procedures to respond independently to messages received through the interfaces. Within the architecture of an object-oriented component, change, such as rehosting, process reengineering, new functionality, and so on, may occur over time. These changes are transparent to the enterprise as a whole as long as the interfaces are maintained in accordance with the established protocols.

Finally, the message-based communications that are inherent in object-oriented models—regardless of how those messages are actually implemented—provide a natural platform for information sharing among components, even when some components still reside within the legacy world and others are now hosted within the target environment. Although it will take time for object-oriented technology to become robust and functionally mature, it will become a clear win. Object-orientation is an obvious way of describing systems in terms of components (i.e., objects) that are distributed.

8.2.2 Openness and Standards

In addition to object orientation, the other key architectural characteristics of cooperative ISs and Chicken Little migrations are openness and standards. Openness simply means that components have published interfaces "openly" connecting them to the other components. More informally, it is taken to mean that any component can communicate with any other component. Hence, a cooperative IS and any legacy IS, for that matter, may be described as "open" when components can be connected with little or no "glue." Only an understanding of the interface and the development of service requests using it are needed.

As with any computing systems, this never happens transparently of the meaning of the component being accessed. That is, interoperability and connectivity require a mutual understanding of the requests and potential responses. This too must be published as well as the interface. You must publish that interface of the component so folks will know how to invoke it. You must also publish the meaning of the operations and data to facilitate understanding of what is being provided by the component. This is typically not represented in the interface, which states simply what functions are available and not what the functions mean.

Openness is achieved primarily through the support of various IS standards across the different service areas: user interface, data management, metadata management, graphics, directory services, communications and networking, and various application-level services, such as electronic mail, messaging, and complex document exchange. Through the adoption and use of standards, several benefits may be achieved:

- greater potential for component reuse (such as when rehosting or subsequent migration occurs)
- fewer required mappings

- less duplication of effort

- less complexity in the overall system when it is fully developed

In general, as we better understand computing, it is easier to compartmentalize computing functions and services into service components. For example, as data management was better understood in the late 1960s, database management was extracted from being an application function to being provided as a service external to and, hence, usable by all applications. This step led to the standardization of database management services. Consequently data management services, previously coded in all applications, became a standardized service never to be programmed by application developers again. This avoided an immense duplication of effort. SQL, the standard database language, made all SQL-conforming database management systems open to all applications. This simplified mappings to databases since it is all done via SQL. Note that to use a standard, open database system, you must know the contents of the database. For applications to be interoperable with the database, they must understand the requests and potential responses accessible via the SQL-connectivity.

Our case studies benefit by having standard SQL connectivity. They can be written on the assumption that all database accesses can be provided through one standard interface. This deals with the technical interoperability. That is, any program can access a DBMS via the standard SQL interface. Being able to use the interface meaningfully in terms of the contents of the database is another matter, the semantic part.

Just as the data management function was extracted from all applications, so should any and all services that could be reused by or shared with other applications. This elegant engineering design principle is at the heart of distributed object computing architectures. Namely, extract from applications all those services that are required to build the application and make each available, independently and transparently, as an infrastructure or object service. This will provide a powerful base for building all applications on a common architecture and set of object services. Ideally, this will reduce applications to those modules (components or objects) essential for describing or implementing application semantics. This same principle could also be applied at the application level. In this way, application modules or objects within an application domain can be reused to the greatest extent possible.

8.2.3 The Enterprise Information Architecture

Given the principles of distributed computing discussed in the previous section, we can then develop an architecture based on those principles to create a framework for Chicken Little incremental migration. Figure 8.2 illustrates an enterprise information architecture built around distributed

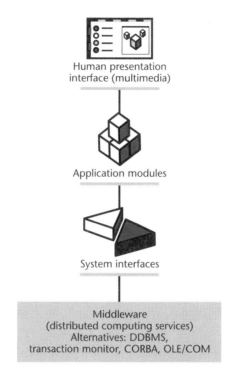

Human presentation
interface (multimedia)

Application modules

System interfaces

Middleware
(distributed computing services)
Alternatives: DDBMS,
transaction monitor, CORBA, OLE/COM

FIGURE 8.2 Enterprise information architecture
and distributed computing services.

computing services. As we described in the previous section, the goal is to extract from all applications those functions that can be used by other applications and provide them as standardized services. In a distributed computing architecture, you would like to use these services independently of where the requesting module resides or where the service-providing module resides. Distributed computing services can be used, transparently, by any application in the distributed computing architecture. This class of software is called middleware, since it resides between the application and the platform (i.e., the operating and communications systems and the hardware).

As illustrated in Figure 8.2, a set of distributed computing services provides the means by which end-user and system applications communicate with underlying physical computer systems. The applications interact, transparently, with the distributed computing services through application programming interfaces, while system interfaces provide the interaction mechanism between the distributed computing services and the physical computer systems, regardless of their location within the enterprise or even outside the enterprise.

133

Ideally, the distributed computing services should be component-oriented in nature and possess the characteristics described in Section 8.1:

- object-oriented to support encapsulation and separation of the interfaces and implementations of the components

- open to facilitate the incorporation of new components with relative ease

- standards-based to facilitate the openness of the system

As described in Section 8.1, a growing number of alternative technologies provide distributed computing services, or middleware. There are many commercial products for each technology alternative. Some of these products are listed here:

CORBA ORB products

- D.O.M.E. from Object-Oriented Technologies

- HP ORB Plus from Hewlett-Packard

- NCR Cooperative Framework from AT&T/NCR

- ObjectBroker from DEC

- Project DOE Developers Release from SunSoft

- Xshell ORB 2.2/3.0 from Expersoft

Microsoft's OLE/COM

DDBMSs

- CA-Ingres/Star from Computer Associates

- DB2 from IBM Corp.

- Informix V7.1 from Informix Corp.

- NonStop SQL from Tandem Computers

- Oracle/Star from Oracle Corp.

- Sybase Navigation Server from Sybase Corp.

Transaction monitors

- Encina from IBM

- Tuxedo from AT&T

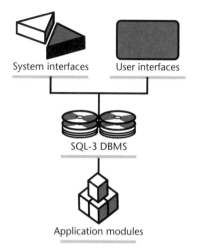

FIGURE 8.3 Current relational DDBMS architecture.

8.3 DISTRIBUTED DATABASE ARCHITECTURES

In this section we describe the distributed database architecture, a significant future distributed computing architecture on which to base the migration and target architecture. Figure 8.3 shows the architecture of current relational distributed database systems.

In the following example, the application submits a DBMS command. Here the goal is to find the names of employees on the first floor:

```
select name
from emp
where dept in
    select dname
    from dept
    where floor = 1;
```

This SQL command is processed by DBMS middleware that is responsible for

- locating the emp and dept objects in the distributed computing environment

- constructing, for the user's command, a heuristically optimal execution plan that will run local queries at the identified sites, interspersed with data movement, and combining the local queries into a single result

- supervising the execution of the command

- returning the result to the application

Execution of the command requires sending local commands to one or more local servers. If the local server understands a different query language from the middleware or a different dialect of SQL, then a gateway is required to translate the command specified by the middleware into a command understood by the local server. The local servers at various sites do the actual work.

Oracle, Sybase, CA-Ingres, Informix, and IBM's DB2 all support the architecture specified in Figure 8.3. They vary significantly with regard to what platforms the middleware runs on and what gateways are supported. However, over time all major relational DBMSs will support hardware *universality* (i.e., they will run on all major hardware and operating system platforms) and *interconnectivity* (i.e., they will have gateways to major current and legacy DBMSs). A brief description and list of database gateways is given in Chapter 10.

Moreover, most relational DBMSs support DDBMS functionality (i.e., distributed transactions and the possibility of replicating objects for enhanced availability). Using these DDBMS features, it is easy to set up the following environment:

- The user interface code and all applications can be replicated at each site in a distributed computing environment.

- Each application can interact with the DDBMS.

If the legacy application is decomposable, if the DDBMS contains a gateway for the particular legacy DBMS (i.e., a reverse gateway), and if the user can construct a forward gateway, then Figure 8.3 is easily particularized into the migration architectures with database gateways that are described throughout the book (e.g., Figures 2.3, 2.5, 3.4).

In summary, in a distributed database architecture, application programs can be run at each site and use a DDBMS to support distribution. This complicates the cutover step since the migration will typically be from a centralized to a distributed architecture. However, the complexity can be overcome by the added benefits of distributed transactions and replication services.

We are assuming that legacy and target data will reside in a database service. Regardless of the distributed computing architecture you select, we propose that the target databases be managed using a commercial DBMS, probably a DDBMS. Hence, these databases must be included in a CORBA-based solution. CORBA provides a bridge to an object database service. But we are not suggesting this as a typical solution. Object DBMSs may be required to support specialized requirements but at the cost of some features in relational DBMSs. On the other hand, relational DBMSs are rapidly moving to object/relational DBMSs that will support many of these requirements without sacrificing any relational DBMS functionality. CORBA provides bridges to relational and other DBMSs (i.e., the query service and the transaction service). Using these services and other CORBA features (e.g., message passing between any objects, such as GUIs, legacy or new applications), the entire target and migration architecture can be created in what we above called the combined architecture. That is, you can implement Figure 8.3 within a distributed computing architecture, such as CORBA, by specifying the DDBMS as a CORBA service.

Over the next several years, the architecture of mainstream DBMSs will change. Specifically, the mainstream vendors will move from SQL-89 to SQL-2 to SQL-3. Most vendors support SQL-2 today and will support SQL-3 when it is finalized by the ANSI committee. SQL-3 has two features of interest to this discussion: 1) It supports an extendible type system, including a variety of type constructors, together with multiple inheritance. 2) It includes user-defined functions (methods) in the DBMS.

These features will permit SQL-3 databases to support, in addition to distributed data and transactions, distributed computation for those methods stored in the DBMS. For example, types such as points, polygons, lines, tiff images, mpeg video, and documents can be specified as SQL-3 data types. In addition, user-defined functions can be defined for these types. Such functions can include

- distance (point, line) returning a float

- contrast-enhancement (tiff image) returning a tiff image

- contains (document, keyword) returning a weight

These functions can be used in SQL-3 commands such as the following, which finds the names of employees who live within three miles of US 101:

```
select name
from emp, roads
where distance (emp.location, roads.position) < 3
and roads.name = "US 101";
```

Moreover, you can define more exotic functions. For example, you can define TPC-A as the following function:

```
TPC-A (account-number, check-amount) returns a Boolean
```

137

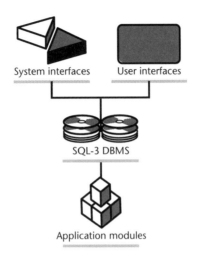

System interfaces   User interfaces

SQL-3 DBMS

Application modules

FIGURE 8.4 Target relational DDBMS architecture.

On the BANK table, the user can then execute the following command:

```
select TPC-A (17, 100)
from BANK;
```

This query will debit account 17 by $100, assuming account 17 appears in the BANK table. Current SQL-3 systems often allow the following shorthand:

```
execute TPC-A (17, 100) on BANK;
```

As such, a user-defined function can be specified that runs within the DBMS and is called (executed) by an application.

Using an SQL-3 system, it becomes feasible and practical to move most or all target applications inside an SQL-3 DBMS as user-defined functions. Hence, user or system interface code talks directly to the DBMS, which in turn calls applications (functions) as necessary, and we get the target IS architecture illustrated in Figure 8.4.

As mainstream DBMS vendors move to SQL-3, then their DDBMSs will automatically support objects and user-defined functions. This will enable the architecture shown in Figure 8.5.

With the picture in Figure 8.5, the user or system interface code talks directly to SQL-3 middleware, which locates data objects of interest as well as user-defined functions, specified in the query. Through a gateway, middleware passes appropriate commands to local DBMSs, which run user-defined functions as necessary. In this way, the location and execution of user-defined

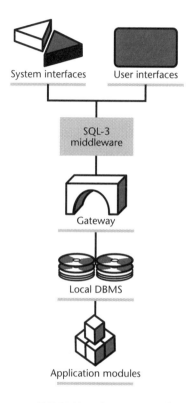

FIGURE 8.5 DDBMS architecture with SQL-3.

functions are under the control of a next-generation DBMS. There is no need for an object service such as CORBA; the functionality is provided by the DBMS.

8.4 CORBA ARCHITECTURES

We now further discuss one possible enterprise information architecture implementation, built around OMG's CORBA.

If you refer back to Figure 8.1, the basic OMG object management architecture features four key architectural components, the object request broker, and the three primary groupings of objects: application objects, common facilities, and object services. It is important to note that CORBA has one basic idea: the ability, through the ORB, to exchange messages between any two objects in the environment. The above groupings of objects are independent of this feature. That is, any object in any group can exchange messages with any others. In this sense CORBA is completely open. The groupings are for conceptual, expository, and management reasons.

Application objects are specific end-user applications. They are components that are not amenable to standardization because of proprietary interfaces and unique functionality, but that must fit into the object management architecture. As described above, ideally they are the applications with all distributed computing services taken out. Application objects are the components that define your business. Examples include end-user applications, such as our cash management modules in CMS (Chapter 3) and our telecom provisioning applications in TPS (Chapter 5).

The common facilities shown in Figure 8.1 are those that have general-purpose capabilities, or those application systems with object-oriented interfaces to common data. These include compound document facilities, user interface facilities, vertical market-specific facilities (e.g., finance, geodata, inventory), system management, and task management. These are likely services that most objects or components require. Therefore, following the above mentioned standardization and reduction of effort motivations, these are provided rather than coded for each application.

Object services are those basic (i.e., core technology) functions needed by objects within the enterprise. In contrast with common facilities, object services are those under the covers or more basic. For example, a user interface system is a high-level facility, whereas event notification, something a user interface system might use, is an object service. Other object services include lifecycle (creation and deletion of objects), naming (mapping of user names to object references), event notification (registration of required and expected notification of event occurrences), persistence, transactions, concurrency, relationships, externalization, queries, and security.

Finally, an ORB provides request and response transmission, using lower-level services, including

- naming services
- parameter encoding
- delivery
- synchronization
- activation
- exception handling
- authentication

8.4.1 Chicken Little Migration on a CORBA Architecture

The distributed computing architecture should be instrumental not only in the Chicken Little migration steps, but also in the design of the target IS. The target IS should be designed as a cooperative IS in which there is a clear separation made between application components, common facilities components, and basic services. Ideally, object services and common facilities can be provided by commercial off-the-shelf packages. For example, all report writing, formatting, editing, etc., should not be coded by applications staff. They should focus their efforts on the components that implement the application-specific functions, policies, and practices of your business—those things that cannot be bought off the shelf. Indeed, significant migration could and should be avoided by replacing legacy code with standardized, component-oriented packages, thus simplifying the entire migration effort, decreasing its risk, and reducing its duration and cost.

As distributed object technology matures and additional products and service interfaces become available, it is suggested that such technology be strongly considered for Chicken Little incremental migration programs. The end result of such efforts will be an open, standards-based, object-oriented enterprise information architecture. Your chances of preventing the recurrence of the legacy system problem will be significantly enhanced. If that is not possible in your organization, we suggest that you hedge your bets. Design the target architecture so that you could migrate easily to a distributed object computing architecture. But bear in mind that avoiding a component-oriented architecture will simply complicate later life.

Global Telecom, the owner of the TPS system discussed in Chapters 5 and 7, has planned to migrate its entire computing architecture consistent with the OMG's CORBA. Figure 8.6 illustrates the target distributed computing architecture. TPS is simply one of many target applications in the target architecture. In fact, what was described as TPS in Chapters 5 and 7 is really one component of a more complex provisioning application suite within the target architecture. The architecture also includes other Global Telecom application suites such as billing, repair, and order entry.

In Figure 8.6, the circles and squares used to represent the applications may be new, possibly object-oriented components, or they could be legacy information systems encapsulated (or wrapped) within object-oriented interfaces. We used circles to suggest object-oriented applications and squares to represent legacy applications. However, from the point of view of an information system requesting a service of these applications, it has no idea of the underlying implementation, and it shouldn't need to know.

We use the term *provisioning suite* here to suggest that there are many forms of provisioning: those provided by the legacy TPS, those currently required by Global Telecom, and those yet to be invented. The provisioning application suite is designed to accommodate changes, such as adding components to support new provisioning services without duplicating those services already in place.

However, the real story is that the vast majority of Global Telecom's applications are, like TPS originally, legacy information systems. The target architecture

141

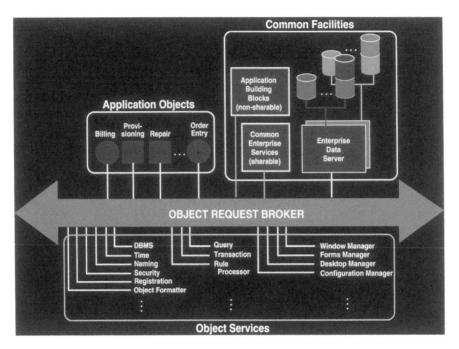

FIGURE 8.6 Global Telecom's target computing architecture.

will initially consist almost entirely of legacy ISs. Figure 8.7 extends the target architecture (Figure 8.6) with an illustration of how legacy applications are attached via the data migration engine and the enterprise data server.

The target architecture and the more likely migration architecture indicate a significant point: legacy IS migration should, by no means, be considered for one legacy IS in isolation. Most information systems, including TPS and CMS from our case studies, must interoperate with many others to meet the information processing requirements of an organization. We recommend that a global plan, such as that illustrated in Figures 8.6 and 8.7, be considered. Then, your organization can develop an incremental plan to migrate the entire computing environment and the associated legacy and new computing resources.

8.4.2 CORBA-Based Application Integration and Migration Frameworks

Since we worked on the case studies described in earlier chapters, there has been a growing trend to recognize the need for Chicken Little migrations and

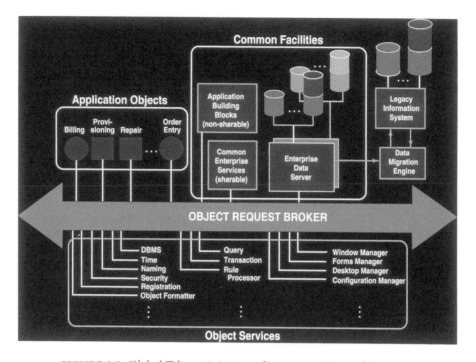

FIGURE 8.7 Global Telecom's intermediate computing architecture.

the necessary environment and support tools. Chapter 10 describes a large number of tools that could be used to support specific steps in the Chicken Little migration. However, we describe here a possibly more useful trend, that is, the development of complete environments to support application integration and legacy IS migration.

A basic requirement of a Chicken Little legacy IS migration is application integration. That is, a Chicken Little migration requires a migration architecture, as introduced in Chapter 1 and elaborated throughout the book. The role of the migration architecture is to facilitate the integration or interoperation of legacy and new applications so that the incremental migration can take place. As described throughout the book, considerably more than the migration architecture is needed. Specifically, we emphasize the need for and function of gateways that decompose and direct calls to the appropriate legacy or new components and then collect, combine, and direct responses to the calling component. A large number of additional tools, as listed in Chapter 10, are also required. But are these tools interoperable? That is, will they work together to support an end-to-end Chicken Little migration? Unfortunately, the answer is no. It is highly unlikely that any two tools you select, as good as they may be individually, will work together. Note that this is the same problem we have always had with our legacy applications. Hence, it is reasonable to assume that the interoperability solution offered by distributed object computing (described earlier in this chapter) should work for the migration environment and the associated tools. Such tools environments and migration architectures are in development. In this section, we review some early commercial products developed to meet such goals.

In principle, such an integration architecture would be provided by a CORBA-compliant ORB. For example, SunSoft claims to support integration of legacy and new applications via its DOE (Distributed Objects Everywhere) product, as does Object-Oriented Technologies, Ltd. with its D.O.M.E. (Distributed Object Management Environment) product. In terms of Chicken Little migrations, these are do-it-yourself kits since they provide the means to interoperate. They all support the development of object-oriented, distributed applications. However, you would have to make your applications interoperable and then incorporate all the necessary tools into that environment. For example, you would have to buy or build the needed gateways and wrapper technology. We have already advised against such challenges unless you are a TP monitor or DBMS vendor. Ideally, gateway vendors are making their products CORBA-compliant. This does not mean that they will interoperate in the specific CORBA product that you may choose, but it does increase the probability that it might or reduce the work to make it do so. NCR Cooperative Framework goes further in that it provides wrapper technology. NCR Cooperative Framework is an ORB-based toolkit that can be used to wrap existing databases and legacy applications for improved interoperability with other components in the integration framework provided by NCR's ORB.

Happily, there are now commercial products that explicitly support application integration by augmenting OMG ORBs with appropriate tools and methodologies. Their goal is to support application integration. In terms of Chicken Little, these products assist significantly with installing the target environment and in developing and installing the migration architecture. These products are called application integration frameworks. Some frameworks go further. They support the design and development of target interfaces, applications, and databases, and possibly the development of some aspects of the required gateways (e.g., wrapping applications and databases). These products are full-fledged application development environments. Still other products support legacy IS migration on top of the migration architecture. We now briefly describe one commercial application integration framework that does not support legacy IS migration, one that does, and mention another that supports legacy database migration only.

Framework-Based Environment (FBE) is Digital's solution for business application integration. It provides a way to integrate and execute cooperative applications that consist of legacy and new applications interoperating with each other. In terms of the Chicken Little migration method, FBE provides what we have called a migration architecture. FBE does not provide support for the incremental migration that might take place on that architecture. However, the migration architecture and the installation of the underlying environment are of major significance and provide a significant basis, in a commercial product, for such a migration. Migration tools, such as those described and listed in Chapter 10, might be used in conjunction with FBE. However, we have not investigated this possibility.

FBE is based on some advanced concepts that are worth describing here since they illustrate the ideas introduced earlier in Chapter 8. These concepts are relatively novel in commercial products and are critical for interoperation between new and legacy applications. We anticipate many other products following these ideas in the near term.

In common with most integration environments, FBE attempts to eliminate point-to-point dependencies between legacy applications by providing an ORB through which all applications communicate. This simple idea underlies distributed object computing, as discussed earlier in this chapter, and specifically underlies the OMG CORBA technology. Indeed, FBE is based on a CORBA product. This facilitates, but does not ensure, plug-and-play between applications. That is, all applications communicate via the ORB and associated services, but there is more to interoperation than sending messages between

A major, unnamed, corporation is, like many others, investigating the development of a global corporate repository as a means for managing its corporate IT resources, primarily in the hope of achieving corporate-wide interoperability. Let's just assume that OMG CORBA technology is in place and ready to go. This very real corporation estimated that they currently have over 40,000 elements (entities, attributes, relationships, applications) defined in existing repository products. They further estimate that, if comprehensive, it would have 75,000 base elements or a total of 100,000 elements if derived data were included. Based on considerable work and experience, they estimated that the total could be reduced to 30,000 to 40,000 if duplicates were removed. Or stated another way, if the corporation were to develop a comprehensive business model, the existing legacy elements could be mapped to it so that the entire computing environment could be described in terms of 30,000 elements. A rough estimate of the time to remodel the data aspects alone is over 1,000 years.

Let's say the above dramatic estimate is wrong. What is the right answer? How many entities does your organization have? How much redundancy is there? How many would be in a nonredundant model? How would you do all the related analysis to answer these questions, let alone carry out the work? How much effort would be required? It's odd that such a global model and the reduction of the legacy model to the new global model is required at some level by many or all of the grand reengineering plans so frequently discussed these days. Yet, most of us have almost no idea what such a model would be like, let alone how to achieve it. Or worse still, no idea of the attendant cost. Given the enormous potential cost of addressing these issues, it is critical to automate the process as much as possible.

applications. Developers still face significant challenges, such as ensuring that the applications mutually understand the messages that they exchange. This is sometimes called semantic interoperability which we mention earlier in this chapter.

Those with experience in applications integration understand the challenges of interoperation at the systems level, which the FBE integration framework and CORBA ORBs are addressing. However, any experience in this area quickly leads to an appreciation of how much more difficult and costly it is to resolve semantic interoperability challenges. For example, how do you ensure a common understanding between 25 separately developed, mission-critical applications, each of which has its own definition of customer, let alone hundreds of other business entities?

Semantic interoperability problems need to be addressed at various levels. For example, FBE addresses the problems at the conceptual or modeling level, as described below. An entire class of products addresses the issues at the data reengineering level. As the nature of and need to address data inconsistency problems is recognized, a number of data reengineering tools are becoming increasingly powerful at helping to resolve some semantic inconsistencies between databases that contain redundant, overlapping, or contradictory information; data errors; inconsistent formats; and the like. Indeed, as we go to press, these tools are taking off in sales to meet the challenges faced by those building data warehouses, an intermediate step before real IS or database integration. To date there have been few legacy ISs or databases migrated with these tools. However, the vendors have described over 50 large-scale migrations underway by early 1995. The Integrity Programming Environment, from Vality Technology, is a data reengineering product designed to address some of these problems. It uses lexical analysis and pattern matching to identify and resolve such problems and fuzzy joins to support the merging of data from different source legacy databases. Integrity and other data scrubbing products, including Apertus' Enterprise/Sync, are described in Chapter 10. Some of these products provide rules and other means (e.g., tables) for identifying and resolving problems. For example, Apertus provides a knowledgebase of such rules that you can augment or specialize to meet your requirements.

DEC's FBE provides a starting point for semantic interoperability issues. The "business-centric integration" approach underlying FBE provides a model and support tools for a solution. However, the solutions to semantic interoperability problems are design-oriented (e.g., establishing agreements as to meanings of and correspondences between entities) and must be done by humans. But FBE provides as much support as we have seen concerning semantic integration of applications. Such approaches are called domain-based or ontology-based and are relatively new. NCR's Cooperative Framework product is also taking this approach. We believe that the domain-based approach is the only feasible one. That is, there must be a deep knowledge of the application domain (e.g., manufacturing, insurance, banking, health care) to be able to identify concepts common to the entire domain (i.e., across all applications in that domain within one organization and, more generally, since organizations need to interoperate, across all organizations in that domain). The development of the relevant domain knowledge is a significant, long-term task that requires considerable domain-specific experience. Hence, the development of such products will take considerable time and investment. We have not had experience with FBE or Cooperative Framework, so we cannot attest to the pragmatic aspects of the products. However, we certainly endorse the concepts.

FBE provides a methodology *MethodF*, which is driven by a business object model. That is, all business entities that are implemented in computing resources or components (e.g., application modules, data stores) are described in terms of objects, independently of whether those resources are legacy or new. This gives a uniform, integrated view to the entire system or collection of systems. FBE supports the mapping of the FBE business objects onto the underlying new or legacy resources. This permits the integrated applications to be seen in a logically homogeneous way, even though the underlying resources may be heterogeneous and distributed. Indeed, the business object model and the mapping to the underlying resources are the means by which developers ensure correct interoperation, not only in terms of communication (i.e., message passing) but also in terms of mutual understanding—the semantic interoperability challenge mentioned above.

The business object model is a simple and powerful concept. It does not require rocket science to integrate concepts via such an object model. It requires conceptual agreement that can be supported by a mapping to the underlying entities being integrated. Establishing this agreement is a design activity done by humans, ideally assisted with tools such as those provided by FBE. What are those tools? Simply stated it is a graphical object definition language supported by FBE's Object Definition Tool (ODT). ODT is essentially James Rumbaugh's Object Modeling Technique with Use Case extensions, from Ivar Jacobson, and other additions that allow FBE to generate CORBA IDL and map the logical model on to physical systems (adapters and implementations). FBE attempts to make the entire specification process graphical.

But there is more to it than that. As a developer, you would like some guidance in identifying common entities. As it often turns out, there are common entities within application domains (e.g., customer, invoice, bill, product). Object-orientation uses this commonality to attempt to permit common entities or types to be reused. So the FBE developers have accumulated their experience in specific application domains and expressed the commonly used entities as types in an object model for that domain. These common entities, expressible as types, form a type hierarchy.

For example, the FBE base object model provides an Exchange type, which is a higher-level type (i.e., the "stateless, abstract supertype") of an Order type.

147

Order has subtypes, which in the manufacturing domain are `Customer Order` (incoming order or an external order to buy something), `Internal Order` (subtypes: `Manufacturing Order` (make it), and `Warehouse Order` (pick it off the shelf)). An incoming `Customer Order` always "decomposes into" other `Customer Orders` and `Internal Orders`. FBE adds states and operations to these "stateless, abstract types" as they become more specialized (i.e., in the industry object models). For example, a simple set of states is added to `Order` (i.e., `canceled`, `placed`, `filled`, etc.). The states `picked` and `packed` are added to `Warehouse Order`, and the corresponding operations, `pick` and `pack`. You can imagine more specialized orders again. For example, FBE is used to describe in a pharmaceutical environment. The `Laboratory Orders` are to perform tests on a batch of drugs that are sent to the lab. FBE specializes the same thing in `Mining`, where a `Laboratory Order` is used to request a sample of crankcase oil from a mining truck to be analyzed to determine whether it is time to change the oil.

So Exchange is in the base object model. `Order` is a subtype in the manufacturing domain. There may be similar types of `Order` in other domains. Within the manufacturing object model, `Order` has three subtypes, `Customer Order`, `Internal Order`, and `Warehouse Order`. In a particular FBE customer environment, there may be further specializations of these types. What is critical here is that FBE provides this predefined set of types with which to describe all applications in the domains for which the object models are proposed.

FBE provides a base object model for all application domains that it might integrate. It provides industry object models for a variety of industries (e.g., manufacturing, pharmaceuticals, mining). FBE also provides means for further specializing these models for FBE customers. The users of FBE may well share concepts with their industry as a whole, but they will likely distinguish themselves in the use of those concepts (e.g., Roche Laboratory Order). The object models are illustrated in the upper left-hand corner of Figure 8.8.

FBE would be used as follows (see Figure 8.8). A modeler would follow the MethodF methodology to guide the design of the Business Object Model. She would appeal to the FBE-supplied base object model and the applicable industry object model as a starting point. You will recognize this as the very best form of reuse: reuse of specifications. The modeler will further specialize the FBE-provided object models to meet the specific requirements of the customer application. This will be expressed using the Object Definition Tool and will result in a object model describing all the objects in the integrated application domain. The model will be used to generate interfaces for the defined objects. The model and the interfaces will be stored in their CORBA repository.

Now let's integrate some applications. A programmer would use the Framework Development Environment, the Repository, and other tools to integrate applications and to develop new applications. The programmer would

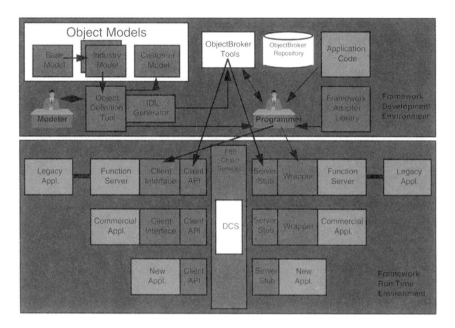

FIGURE 8.8 FBE. *(Courtesy of Digital Equipment Corporation.)*

integrate a legacy application into the environment by being provided, in the Repository, a description of the relevant objects. He would then use an FBE adapter development tool and library of previously defined adapters to wrap or encapsulate the legacy application so as to present the appropriate resources within the legacy application as a collection of objects. The ObjectBroker Tools and other CORBA technology (e.g., IDL compilers) can now be used to establish the mapping between the business model objects and the adapter objects that facilitate access to the underlying legacy application resources. This interconnection is part of the FBE Framework Run Time Environment illustrated in the lower portion of Figure 8.8.

Legacy applications developed by an individual organization (as opposed to an industry standard) pose the greatest challenges for integrating into such environments. They are unlikely to have been developed according to industry standards. Or, as described in earlier chapters, they may be nondecomposable or semidecomposable. Hence, Figure 8.8 illustrates legacy applications with the greatest layering between them and the FBE object services and the core ORB. For example, a function server may be necessary to permit legacy functions to be accessed from the current environment (e.g., it may not be accessible in the client/server environment) or for legacy functions to be called individually (i.e., to deal with the non- or semidecomposable aspects of the legacy application).

149

Hopefully, legacy commercial applications may be better structured or may adhere to industry standards, thus requiring fewer layers to wrap and correspondingly less work. New applications will hopefully offer the least work to integrate since they will be developed based on the architectural principles underlying FBE.

By early 1995, DEC's experience with FBE, primarily in manufacturing, was that 75% of the models have been built using their object models and 25% have been extensions built to accommodate the customer systems. They are not sure if this level of reuse can be achieved in other domains. Integration projects are long term. Almost all projects are still in process with some smaller examples completed and in production. The larger examples are on the scale of the systems used to run a factory.

ObjectStar provides an integrated architecture and a development environment. The architecture permits legacy applications—both on-line and batch, 3GL and assembly language applications residing on MVS mainframes as well as UNIX 3GL systems—to interoperate with cooperative, object-oriented, distributed client/server applications residing on a range of UNIX and other platforms, including Sun's running Solaris, RS6000s running AIX, and HP workstations running HP/UX, NT, OS/2, and Windows. The proprietary development environment supports the development of cooperative, distributed client/server applications using ObjectStar rules and object-oriented methods.

ObjectStar directly supports a Chicken Little-like migration methodology. It supports the partitioning of large legacy ISs into components and selectively and incrementally migrating the components to the client/server environment. As advocated in Chicken Little, you can control the rate at which the legacy IS is migrated to the target environment. As described throughout the book, the intermediate or transition architecture involves legacy code that has not yet been migrated, coexisting and interoperating with newly developed target code residing in the client/server environment, or, as an option within ObjectStar, on the mainframe. ObjectStar permits target code to be deployed on the server or desktop to control the migration and balance performance issues.

As described throughout the book, many challenges arise in these complex legacy IS migrations. Where possible and available, advanced technology should be used instead of home-grown technology, particularly in the case of gateways and transaction monitors. ObjectStar claims to address many issues that we raised concerning gateways and their transaction requirements (see Sections 1.7 and 2.4). It supports read and write access to legacy and new databases using ObjectStar's own transaction processing monitor. It ensures two-phase commit necessary for update coordination across multiple databases.

ObjectStar provides support for incremental migration of legacy databases to target databases. It provides operators to extract qualified data subsets from legacy databases and places them into the ObjectStar repository, MetaStor. MetaStor then provides applications with a logical view of data, thus hiding

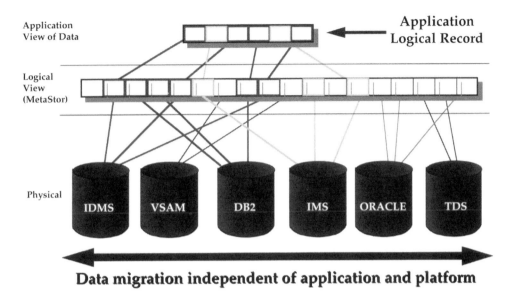

Application View of Data

Application Logical Record

Logical View (MetaStor)

Physical

IDMS VSAM DB2 IMS ORACLE TDS

Data migration independent of application and platform

FIGURE 8.9 ObjectStar data transparency. *(Courtesy of Antares Alliance Group.)*

from them the details of whether the data is in legacy or target databases, as illustrated in Figure 8.9. This transparency permits the data migration to proceed independently of the applications. This independence between applications and databases is critical for a Chicken Little incremental migration. For a target database, ObjectStar provides a relational DBMS that supports distributed data. ObjectStar permits data extracted from legacy data stores into MetaStor to be written to the relational database, thus achieving the desired migration.

ObjectStar has opened its proprietary environment to support OLE, ODBC, and a published C/C++ interface. OLE and OBDC are currently at the desktop level. The C/C++ interface is available at all implementation levels, whether it be the mainframe server or the desktop. As with the other products mentioned in this section, a commercially available ORB is embedded in ObjectStar as the mechanism for communication between the server levels and the desktop.

According to the Antares Alliance Group, as of early 1995 over 10 large-scale legacy ISs have been successfully migrated using ObjectStar. Over 1,000 migrations are in process. Over the past five years, we have heard of only a handful of other such legacy IS migrations worldwide. So this trend toward real, successful legacy IS migrations and the initiation of such projects is very significant. Presumably, this means that the need for legacy IS migrations has finally become significant enough to overcome the problems that have prevented such projects, described in Chapter 1. Further, it may mean that the legacy IS migration process as described in this book has become understood and accepted and that powerful supporting concepts and technology, outlined here and in Chapter 10, are mature enough to support at least some aspects of legacy IS migration.

Given the increasing problems and cost of legacy ISs and the potential advantages of advanced technologies such as distributed object computing, it is highly likely that the trend described in this section will continue to grow. That is, we expect that comprehensive environments will be offered commercially to support the twin challenges of taking advantage of advanced information technologies and dealing appropriately with the highly valuable but poorly packaged legacy already in place. We hope that such environments will support all aspects of the Chicken Little migration method, including the integration or migration architecture (including support for installing the target environment); gateways with transaction support; wrapping technology to encapsulate legacy resources; tools for the analysis and extraction of specifications for legacy data and procedures; tools to decompose or improve the structure of legacy data and procedures; tools to assist with incremental data migration including scrubbing, transformation and bulk download and upload; tools for the design and development of target interfaces, applications, and databases; and, with all this complexity, tools for testing, configuration management, and cut over to the target resources. Chapter 10 provides a description of all these tools and provides lists of specific tools available at the time of publication. Our hope is that these tools will be enhanced, so that they meet the functional requirements described in the book, and will be portable and interoperable, so that they could be used in any migration environment and with any combination of complementary tools.

DBStar Migration Architect is an automated data engineering toolset that can analyze and consolidate diverse data sources into a coherent, enterprise model or database design. It is intended to automate significant portions of legacy database migration. It supports the analysis of legacy databases from which it deduces data integrity rules (largely functional dependencies) and data types, which it uses to form an "as is" data model (i.e., a schema for the legacy database). It uses the "as is" schema and the integrity rules to assist with the reengineering and migration of the schema to form a target relational database schema from which it can largely automatically produce a physical schema. Hence, DBStar's significant contribution is to translate the data model or schema, thus providing a target database, a very significant step in legacy database migration. The step it does not support is legacy data extraction and migration to the target database.

8.5 CLOSING REMARKS

We have discussed distributed computing architectures as the potential target and migration architectures for Chicken Little migration. We identified four alternative technologies with which to create such an architecture, and we discussed the limitations and benefits of each. There is no clear winner, except perhaps distributed databases in the near term and a combined architecture in the long term. We concluded the chapter with a discussion of two new products that provide, in addition to target and migration architectures, frameworks for distributed application integration and, in one case, legacy IS migration. These frameworks and a complementary tool, DBStar, provide support for dealing with semantic interoperability, which we introduced in this chapter. Semantic interoperability is a challenge that cannot be avoided in any legacy IS migration and is more challenging than systems interoperability supported, to varying degrees, by each of the architectural alternatives.

Chapter 9

TOOL WISH LIST

Some tasks (e.g., dealing with semantic interoperability, schema integration, data reengineering) are not ultimately amenable to automation. Considerable human interaction and decision making is required. Much research has yet to be done to understand these areas, let alone to produce tools to effectively address them. For most legacy IS migration steps, there are almost no adequate tools or techniques. Those that exist do not scale up to meet the challenges posed in the understanding, decomposition, integration or recomposition, design, development, maintenance, or evolution of large-scale ISs.

In this chapter, we point out areas in which we hope to see further research and development.

Our experience with Global Telecom's TPS and Money Central's CMS led us to compose the following wish list. This wish list comments briefly on technologies and tools that could dramatically help the migration steps described in the book. Almost all of these suggestions require research. The good news is that, in recent years, tools have begun to appear in these areas.

9.1 Gateways

Gateways are critical to all migration methods and architectures proposed in this book. Gateways—sometimes called surround technology—enable a legacy component to seamlessly migrate to its corresponding target component. For example, CMS uses a gateway to gracefully move from legacy VSAM files to the target DBMS technology without a discontinuous break. The use of gateways is crucial and unavoidable; however, they pose great technical challenges and can be extremely costly to build and operate. Indeed, we recommend that they be designed and built by database systems or transaction processing experts. It would be enormously valuable to develop generic gateway technology to encapsulate databases, interfaces, communications, or any other major system component.

Gateway functionality can go far beyond transaction management, a key feature described in this book and one that is lacking in most gateway products. A gateway must capture calls of a variety of kinds, often specific to the legacy IS; understand the calls; and decompose them into calls to the appropriate legacy or target components underneath the gateway. It must ensure that updates to copies of data are transactional. Then it must collect the results of calls to the underlying components and compose them into a single response, which is then directed to the calling legacy or target component. In addition, the gateway must handle errors in calls to the gateway and in responses received for the underlying components. For database gateways, this is similar to a DDBMS manager. However, database gateway products do not support the capture and analysis of specific legacy IS calls, nor do they support the data or command translation necessary for generating the database calls that existing products do handle. To adequately support the functions required for Chicken Little migrations, existing database gateway products must be extended.

> Chapter 10 describes and lists the existing tools that support steps in legacy IS migrations. However, the area of legacy IS migration is relatively new, as are the products described and listed in Chapter 10. As with most new products and ideas, most of these tools and frameworks are not as mature or as complete as we might like. After all, if there have been only a handful to, at most, 50 successful legacy IS migrations worldwide, you can imagine that the lack of practical experience has yet to flesh out the tools.

Although we understand the theory and functions of database gateways, we don't understand the theory underlying application or IS gateways. Database gateways deal solely with calls to database services. Although there can be quite a variety, they are easily understood by database experts. Application gateways deal with application calls. Not only are there a vastly greater number of possible call types for applications, the calls involve application-

> Gateway functionality can go far beyond transaction management.

specific semantics. Hence, the application gateway must do much more to understand, decompose, and so on. In addition, the understanding must involve the application semantics that make such gateways labor-intensive. For example, the gateway must understand the semantics of the calls of each application using the gateway. IS gateways deal with capturing presentation-layer semantics and translating them into calls to underlying legacy and target components. All the gateway functions mentioned above must be supported, but at the IS gateway level, with very little information. An IS gateway is more complex than a database gateway but less complex than an application gateway.

Gateways are broadly applicable to IS architectures. Their use extends far beyond their role in migration architectures. In fact, they may become major components of future IS architectures. Whenever two systems are required to interact, some interface is required. If the interactions involve anything more than simple remote procedure calls, it is often necessary to develop a software interface component between the two systems—a gateway. Gateways have stringent requirements. For example, those between mission-critical ISs must be very reliable, robust, and efficient. They cannot impose a significant performance penalty on the old IS (say more than 10%). It is not clear how to achieve this level of performance.

Requirements for IS interaction (often misleadingly called IS integration) and distributed computing (e.g., client/server) are growing dramatically. Gateways are a frequently proposed solution. Indeed, some proposals for next-generation computing (e.g., OMG) are based on gateways. Research is required to understand and develop generic gateway technology. There is an increasing number of ad hoc (i.e., for a small number of specific systems) gateway products currently with minimal functionality (e.g., no update coordination). General-purpose tools are required for constructing gateways, just as DBMSs are generic tools for constructing data-intensive applications. Ad hoc gateways are extremely complex and costly to construct. This can be seen in the cost and complexity of gateways provided by DBMS vendors to support heterogeneous DDBMSs focused on their product.

9.2   SPECIFICATION EXTRACTORS

Specifications for legacy ISs are nearly nonexistent. For both CMS and TPS, the code itself is almost the only documentation. In narrow domains such as banking, it may be practical to write a program that extracts specifications from the old code. Such a tool would help immensely in decrypting modules to be rewritten. Research along this line has been done under the name of redocumentation; see the article by Wong et al. (*IEEE* 1995b).

9.3 APPLICATION ANALYZERS

Current code analyzers are adept at determining statistics for a given application (e.g., number of lines of code, call graph). Although this information is valuable, next-generation tools could do much more. A code analyzer could inspect the modules in a large system and determine metrics for difficulty of module migration. Such metrics are probably not statistical in nature, as are the current quality metrics used in software engineering. Rather, they are more akin to an expert system that knows about the difficulties in porting software to a new environment. Such a tool could assist the CMS and TPS migrations immeasurably. Code understanding is receiving increasing attention in the past five years. See the articles by Ning et al., Markosian et al., and Biggerstaff et al. (*ACM* 1994) listed in the references.

9.4 DEPENDENCY ANALYZERS

It would be valuable to have a tool that would inspect two modules, *A* and *B*, to ascertain if one did, or did not, depend on the other. Although it is straightforward to construct a call graph of a complex application, a powerful dependency analyzer would also inspect global variables and the reading and writing of auxiliary data structures, such as files. The best dependency analyzer would be able to guarantee that a module *A* was not dependent on another module *B*, so that the latter one could be replaced by a rewritten one without fear of application collapse.

9.5 MIGRATION SCHEMA DESIGN AND DEVELOPMENT TOOLS

For both CMS and TPS, the structure and design of the legacy database had to be deduced largely from the legacy code. As a result of legacy design techniques, data descriptions are distributed throughout the code and are often indistinguishable from application code. These factors and the lack of documentation make database design difficult. An additional database design problem is the design of the migration schema. The migration schema must provide a mapping from the legacy database to the target database.

A migration schema integrates the legacy and target schemas. It would be a great help to have tools that help to both analyze data definitions in legacy ISs and design the migration schema. This may draw on results from schema integration and conceptual modeling research and products. Although the motivating problems are critical and some of the results useful, most results and related products are almost completely inadequate in providing solutions to real design problems posed by real legacy ISs. For example, some legacy data understanding products (e.g., Bachman's Tool Set) can extract data descriptions from legacy code, assist with evolving it to more abstract levels (e.g., logical and conceptual), and help in generating target schemas (e.g., conceptual, logical, and physical). However, these products do not maintain the information needed to map the corresponding data from the legacy database to the target—what we have called the migration schema.

Until recently, the most that existing products provide for in automatic mapping between two schemas are suggestions that a data element in one schema matches an element in another schema, based on simple text matching of the data element names. DBStar Migration Architect claims to do considerably more. DBStar analyzes actual legacy data to deduce the legacy schema. It also assists in developing a target logical and physical schema, using integrity rules that it deduced from the legacy database. It further assists with the migration of the legacy data to the target relational database. DBStar has reported successful legacy database migrations for large-scale databases.

9.6   DATABASE EXTRACTORS

Legacy databases tend to be ill-structured and contain significant problems (e.g., TPS's broken pointer chains). They also tend to be vast. In TPS, a considerable amount of data is solely an artifact of the implementation and need not be migrated. It would be very effective to have tools that could extract data from the legacy database, repair it if necessary, validate it against the migration database, ignore it if it were not relevant, translate relevant data to the required formats, and load it into the target DBMS. Following the Chicken Little strategy, all of this should be done incrementally (i.e., migrate a logical/physical subset of the database at a time). Antares Alliance Group's ObjectStar supports some aspects of incremental legacy database migration.

Since legacy databases contain large amounts of corrupted data, such a tool would have to be augmented with powerful, automated mechanisms for dealing with exceptions, errors, and other problems. A growing number of data scrubbing products (e.g., Apertus Technologies' Enterprise/Sync) and data reengineering products (e.g., Vality's Integrity Programming Environment) supporting some of the above functions are just beginning to be offered.

Semantic interoperability is one of the least-appreciated challenges in legacy database migration and possibly one of the most costly to resolve. Understanding the semantics of one database at the schema and data levels is a massive job. It is a job that humans must do, for the most part. Deciding how to integrate two databases, at the schema and data levels, is also a mostly human task. The best you can do here is to

> Semantic interoperability is one of the least appreciated challenges in legacy database migration.

159

A legacy database integration and migration was attempted on two vast legacy databases. Because of the lack of tools at the time (1994), much of the work was done manually by database and application experts. Based on the experience and time taken to integrate and migrate half of the schema, it was estimated that the integration and migration of each entity would take an expert in excess of five hours. This does not include dealing with the attributes. Then database scrubbing and transformation tools were used in a pilot to integrate and migrate 20% of the corresponding data (note: 20% of the data for 50% of the entities). The ultimate cost of this part of the pilot was five times what had been budgeted with the advice of the tool vendor. Since 1994 the data scrubber and data reengineering tool vendors claim to have significantly improved their products. Good! Let's see.

automate the process as much as possible, provide tools to assist the human trying to understand, and map one or more schemas from the legacy database service to the target.

Don't forget that most legacy databases do not have schemas. Depending on the legacy database service, the challenges can be immense. For example, in IBM's IMS, considerable application semantics have been, probably inappropriately, embedded in the IMS database. If not in the actual data, then they've been embedded in the access paths, segments, indexes, and the like. Database migration requires some separation of the semantics of data from the semantics of the applications that share the data. We could go on and on about this problem because it is so little understood. Few people realize the cost of this step alone.

Again, database reengineering or database migration are areas requiring deeper understanding and research. Recent articles on the topic include those by Aiken et al. and Premerlani and Blaha (*ACM* 1994).

9.7 HIGHER-LEVEL 4GLs

Our migration proposals included incrementally rewriting most of CMS and TPS in a 4GL. To make this as financially digestible as possible, the leverage relative to COBOL and FORTRAN must be made as large as possible. Although the current figure of merit (20:1 improvement) makes rewriting practical, it would be more attractive with higher-level tools. What such a 5GL or similar high-level programming language would consist of is an open research question.

9.8 DISTRIBUTED SYSTEMS DESIGN AND PERFORMANCE TESTING

Sizing of new hardware has been a back-of-the-envelope exercise in the case studies talked about here. In distributed systems, the distributed hardware design is critical. It is dependent on data and application or object distribution, which in turn is based on the workload and the intended communication traffic. These factors affect not only performance but also potential points of failure and the corresponding recovery mechanisms. These factors, in part, determine the hardware necessary at each site.

Although it is easy to distribute data and processing over multiple jelly bean systems, it would be desirable to have a performance analyzer that could predict response time for the CMS and TPS transaction loads using a planned schema on a particular hardware design. Such sizing studies are time consuming and could be aided by a powerful tool. The old adage, Load a large database early and benchmark your high-volume interactions, should be replaced by advice that is cheaper and easier to follow.

> The old adage, Load a large database early and benchmark your high-volume interactions, should be replaced by advice that is cheaper and easier to follow.

9.9 APPLICATION CUTOVER

The CMS and TPS migrations require several critical cutovers. In a large terminal (or PC) network, it is unrealistic to move instantly from one IS to another. It would be very helpful to find a graceful way to move a few users at a time to a new environment. Research is required into methods and tools to support smooth, incremental cutover from legacy to target IS components while the IS is under continuous operation.

9.10 DISTRIBUTED IS DEVELOPMENT AND MIGRATION ENVIRONMENT

Distributed client/server computing is very popular, and an increasingly large number of concepts, tools, and techniques are being provided. It would be highly desirable to have a consistent environment that supports the development of distributed ISs. Since future distributed ISs will include components of legacy ISs and will continuously evolve, the environment should also support the migrations described in this book.

The environment should support the integration of arbitrary tools. It should provide a collection of tools to support the design, development, testing, deployment, and management of databases, applications, and user interfaces that will be distributed over a target environment. Besides the tools described above, the environment might also include tools for optimal distribution of code and data, database optimization, and distributed transaction design.

9.11 MIGRATION PLANNING AND MANAGEMENT

The composite IS that exists during migration is more complex than its component legacy or target ISs. Because of the mission-critical nature of ISs and the cost of errors, this complexity requires careful management. The key migration challenges involve planning and managing the process. These include selecting the increments to be migrated, interleaving the largely independent steps, and sequencing the steps to diminish risk of failure. These are currently entirely intuitive decisions. As the many different interfaces, applications, and database migrations proceed in parallel and are cut over in stages with both legacy and target versions, there will be many versions to manage.

Migration planning for TPS and CMS are very complex processes that must be managed, since they are both for mission-critical, operational ISs. CMS and TPS are both so complex that no one person or small group of people understands the entire system. Because of their mission-critical nature, some aspects of migration planning and management should be automated. We believe that the infrastructure for future ISs must support continuous migration (i.e., evolution). Hence, support for evolution (called migration here) planning, management, and development must become an integral part of those infrastructures.

9.12 MORE INFORMATION ON TOOLS

For further information on and comparisons of tools, see periodicals such as *Datamation*, *PC Week*, and *Computerworld*. For a more detailed examination of tools, consider the following:

- A survey entitled "Reengineering Tools Report," published by the U.S. Air Force's Software Technology Support Center at Hill Air Force Base in July, 1992. Call (801) 777-8045. The same group maintains a reference database on tools, which has been used in U.S. Department of Defense projects and others. They also publish *Crosstalk*, a newsletter covering software-engineering and reengineering topics for a diverse audience.

- *Software Maintenance News*, which publishes a comprehensive, well-indexed reengineering and maintenance tools survey as the "Software Maintenance Technology Reference Guide." Call (415) 969-5522.

Chapter 10

A PRACTICAL IMPLEMENTATION WITH MIGRATION TOOLS

BY JENNIFER SCHMIDT

Many steps of the Chicken Little migration method can benefit from the use of tools. This chapter categorizes the multitude of migration tools and helps you to choose the tools that best fit your requirements. The function of each tool category, along with its benefits or limitations, is discussed. Then the tool categories are matched to those Chicken Little migration steps where they can be most useful. A series of tables provide information about tools on the market at the time of publication.*

10.1 USING TOOLS

The migration of legacy ISs is often a long and complex process, but it yields results that can have significant payback. Migration tools can help you in this process. Tools automate steps, shorten project duration, and provide project consistency through the use of documentation. Certain tools, such as gateways and configuration management products, play a more significant role than others.

---

* The information in this chapter is correct to the best of our knowledge. However, the mention of any specific product in this book does not constitute an endorsement of that product or offer any assurance of availability or of product features and functionality.

It is important to note up front that tools, no matter their significance, never drive the migration process. The Chicken Little methodology is the process driver, and the tools simply automate steps in the process. Furthermore, few tools can automate each migration step, and those that do exist are limited in what they automate.

There is no silver bullet when it comes to legacy IS migration. No one tool or tool framework exists that automates a migration from soup to nuts. However, frameworks such those described in Chapter 8 are aspiring to this goal. The available migration tools automate specific steps, with some of them automating more steps than others. For example, one database migration tool automates the migration of data structures, data definitions, and procedural I/O, whereas another automates just data structure migration. If the process were simple and the tools available, legacy IS migration would be easy and commonplace.

10.1.1 Tool Limitations

The Chicken Little migration method has 11 steps. You will need multiple tools for the multiple steps, many times even multiple tools for each step. However, a significant limitation in using multiple tools is their lack of coordination. Ideally, a framework of tools should be able to interoperate to exchange data or metadata such as data descriptions. Through the deployment of intertool coordination, the possibilities of invoking the functions in other tools or communicating with one or more databases are made a reality. Unfortunately, few tool vendors have yet to begin addressing the need for interoperability. Without coordination among multiple tools, your job is more difficult.

The use of multiple tools adds an extra layer to project complexity. There are associated methodologies and standards for training, implementation, and operation that vary according to tool specifics. These standards and methodologies must be considered before any product implementation, because the tools alone do not automate cross-product coordination. Project management and configuration tools can help with multiple tool coordination, but some manual interfacing is required between product lines.

Additional manual effort is required if your application portfolio contains some of the less-employed platforms, databases, and programming languages. You will find fewer, if any, tools that support these environments. A number are certain to support the many COBOL and DB2 applications, but fewer alternatives exist for Natural and Adabas applications.

Complex reengineering processes also have less tool support. For instance, application analysis can be aided by a variety of static and dynamic analyzers that extract data and procedure functionality. For more complex processes, such as reverse engineering, fewer tools are available.

10.1.2   Future Directions

Future tool development will likely focus on the integration of functions into a single suite of tools, permitting tool interoperability. Tools with similar functions will be grouped together within a framework that supports common operations. I expect that there will be frameworks facilitating the use of a wide variety of tools. These frameworks will be design/development environments that will support the addition of new tools as needed or as they become available. In addition, these frameworks will reduce the number of assorted products and relieve the coordination efforts.

As the popularity of distributed computing continues, the number of products that reengineer legacy applications into distributed applications will grow. This is evidenced by the tools that exist today. Only a small number of migration tools existed a few years ago, and reengineering tools were strictly for restructuring spaghetti applications. Today, reengineering tools migrate as well as maintain existing systems, and application development tools generate new applications as well as migrate legacy systems. This trend continues with increased automation and other product features that facilitate migration.

10.2   TOOL CATEGORIES

The migration tools on the market today handle functions as diverse as screen scrapping to full-scale reverse engineering. Matching your tool requirements to existing tools can be a confusing process. Organizing tools by function can help you to select the tools most appropriate for your needs. The tools for the practical implementation of migration projects fall into five functional categories:

- gateways
- analyzers and specification extractors (both data and procedure)
- migration tools
- testing tools
- configuration management tools

The following sections describe each category in detail. Depending on your requirements, it's possible that you will be choosing one or more tools from each category. It's also possible that you will elect to hire a full-service migration consultant. A full-service migration consultant can provide you with expert consultants to choose the tools and then supervise the migration.

10.2.1 Gateways

A gateway is a software module introduced between operational software components to mediate between them and insulate components from changes being made to other components. A typical gateway links a mainframe to a PC or distributed environment. As Brodie and Stonebraker stress throughout the book, gateways play a key role in any migration architecture. Every IS migration requires the use of at least one and most likely several gateways. Gateways can be designed and developed internally, purchased through commercially available packages, or exist as a combination of the two.

The purpose of the gateway in the Chicken Little migration architecture is to provide a bridge between the legacy IS and target environments. During the migration process, a gateway allows the interfaces, applications, or data to be migrated incrementally, transparently to the user. The connection is achieved by translating information in a forward direction, from the legacy to the target, and in a reverse direction, from the target to the legacy.

The functions of a gateway are critical when migrating interface, data, or other system components from the legacy to the target environment. An IS gateway is the most complex type, because it encompasses the entire functions of the legacy IS. The IS gateway channels all information between the user and the IS. For example, a screen-scrapping tool captures existing screen images and translates them to IS requests to the appropriate legacy or target components (e.g., applications or databases). It also receives responses from the components and combines them into a single response, which it then displays to the user. The IS gateway is also used to migrate the user interface, for example, from a text screen to a GUI or to a multimedia front end. The IS gateway is used in migrations where the legacy IS is nondecomposable; that is, it is impossible to separate application functions from database services. An application gateway receives requests from interface components, decomposes them as required, and directs subrequests to the appropriate target or legacy application components. The application gateway also coordinates the execution of the subrequests (e.g., update coordination) and combines the results into a single response to the client user interface components. A database gateway is placed between the database service and the application modules. It captures calls and translates recognizable I/O statements in a forward or reverse direction. Any or all of these gateways might be used in a migration project. Whatever the gateway used, its functions should be transparent to the programmer, program, or user.

The gateway is one of the first components installed. The load on the gateway is likely to start small, since at first only a few target components exist, and increase as the migration effort picks up and more components are in the target environment. The design of the gateway architecture should support the anticipated activity. Gateway design should also anticipate traffic after migration completes, because the gateway usually remains as a permanent structure in the IS architecture. This is because some legacy components may not be migrated. The reliability of the gateway is extremely important. If a gateway crash occurs, all mainframe and LAN users on the gateway are affected. Ideally, a user should not experience a large amount of downtime or noticeable performance degradation.

Many types of gateways exist on the market. Some of these products pertain specifically to databases, applications, or a combination of both. The more complex your gateway requirements are, the higher the probability you will need to enhance a commercially available product or develop one. Most of the gateways Brodie and Stonebraker have encountered are direct SQL-to-SQL translators or some other form of database language-to-database language converter. Most simply handle language-to-data translation without addressing transaction management, a necessary element if the gateway is to support updates across the legacy and target DBMSs.

Earlier in this section, two responsibilities of a gateway in a migration project were identified: insulation and mediation between software components. A third responsibility, coordination between the components, is where most commercial gateway products fall short. Most existing products provide no way of ensuring that the data is consistent between the legacy and target DBMSs. Data consistency is crucial when you are migrating an entire database and are likely to have some data in the legacy and some in the target.

10.2.2 Analyzers and Specification Extractors

Analyzers and specification extractors use of wide variety of techniques to assess the technical, functional, and architectural aspects of an application, program, or database. At an application level they provide a bird's eye view of an entire system, showing flowcharting, metrics, code quality, and file usage. The application analyzers are typically static analyzers—they run in the background—because of the large amount of information they process. The results populate a repository where reports can then be generated. With the graphical capabilities of the PC or front-end analyzing tools, a dynamic view of an entire system or program is possible. At the system level, these dynamic analyzers provide flowcharting and system-wide cross-referencing. At a program level, the real strength of dynamic analyzers is tracing through source code execution. A user steps through a simulated execution of a program or group of programs, going backward as well as forward.

Data analysis features are usually packaged within the application and program analyzer tools, but they also exist individually as full, robust tools. Data analysis starts by tracing name assignments for a single entity as it passes through an entire system. During the tracing process, tools are able to locate all data name aliases. The identification of aliases then leads to a rationalization process where all names for one data entity are assigned a common, more suitable name. This procedure is part of what is known as data scrubbing—an important step before migrating to a new database. The use of these tools also shows an overall synopsis of the impact data modifications will make. Repository products offer similar analysis features for the information they contain. They document existing data relationships and aid the forward engineering effort into new databases.

The process of extracting specifications, or reverse engineering, is difficult. Tools with the ability to extract reliable application specifications from legacy ISs are nearly nonexistent. The lack of tools stems from the complexity of the process. In many of the instances where specifications were extracted, it was largely a manual effort. On the data side, reverse engineering tools do exist, and there are instances where these tools have been used successfully to reverse engineer data into new environments (e.g., relational), but this is not a small effort. Reverse engineering tools for data are quite successful with schemas but much less successful with migrating the corresponding data. The cost and complexity of data migration is always vastly underestimated. Reverse engineering the code is an even greater challenge. Vendors of application generators have been experiencing more success by reverse engineering the legacy code to an intermediate meta language and then regenerating the application in the target environment. However, Brodie and Stonebraker recommend tossing legacy code and rewriting, using advanced programming tools and environments that often produce 20:1 productivity increases over conventional programming.

Analyzers and specification extractors automate the gathering of system documentation where little, if any, exists. Application analyzers at a high level benefit both data and procedure migration. For data migration, the use of program analyzers supplements data analysis and automates the tracing of data definitions and usage among application procedural logic.

Although data and procedure analyzers are useful for system documentation, the hard part is knowing what to do with the information. These steps are not always apparent and take some time to establish, but automating the documentation gathering is better than manually performing the effort. You should note that the information these tools gather identifies logic flow, which is not a substitute for manually gathering function specifications.

Repository load modules are nice for documenting enterprise data structures and loading databases, but the information has to be loaded into the repository. These steps are not usually automated and, therefore, changes are not automatically reflected. The information must be loaded manually. That makes the process very costly and time-consuming. For these reasons, data repositories, once very popular, have not been widely used. Tools, like static and dynamic analyzers, are typically the best choice to provide documentation in the decomposition of systems.

10.2.3 Migration Tools

Migration tools enable the automation of migration increments once the target architecture is in place. There are tools that automate increments of interface, data, and application migration, and some that automate everything. Interface migration is usually the easiest. The migration of an interface to a target architecture could be as simple as capturing the character interface at execution and translating it to a graphical representation, or the replacement of the character interface by inputting it into a converter to generate a new graphical interface. In application migration, a program or group of programs is transferred and compiled for execution in the target environment. The more complex data migration includes new design, data structure conversion, data scrubbing, and data transport.

Interface migration was the first form of client/server migration. Several tools were introduced that took existing screen images at execution time and translated them into a graphical appearance. It was a relatively quick and easy way to see a change, but it didn't provide many of the benefits of a distributed system. Now the character screens are replaced by inputting them into products that generate graphical substitutes. Increased editing capabilities allow modifications and the addition of other graphical elements. With object-oriented techniques gaining popularity, these tools are focusing on the visual aspects of screen creation and execution.

Tool development for application migration has focused on downloading procedural logic and business functions. Through the use of COBOL and other PC frameworks, business functions can be downloaded and recompiled to execute in a new environment. If there are no changes in programming languages, the compilers on the different platforms, with some exceptions, are similar. In a continuing effort to make reverse engineering successful, vendors of client/server development environments keep trying to incorporate portions of legacy business functions into their environments. They have not had much success in this area.

Frameworks are also useful for data migration. Most of the COBOL frameworks imitate popular databases, such as DB2, IMS, and IDMS, or there are available PC versions of these mainframe products. Middleware products that provide all communication and database translation between application components are another alternative for migrating data. The use of middleware has allowed some organizations to gain the benefits of client/server while they are still in the process of migrating to a new database, as proposed with the Chicken Little migration strategy.

Database migration, especially migration of database definitions, is the most complex of the migration processes. The concepts of a hierarchical database, like IMS, are extremely different from those of a relational database, like DB2. The data definitions need reengineering to a new design. Data reengineering extracts existing data definitions and stores them in an intermediate

169

form that modeling tools can reuse and then forward engineer. This process takes a substantial amount of time, even with tool automation. The same concepts apply to data scrubbing, a process that rids existing data of redundancies and other anomalies. Before actually migrating data to a new database, it should be cleaned of the many inconsistencies, redundancies, and anomalies that have crept in through the years.

The available tools, with a few exceptions, do not deal with semantics. The semantics of an application, particularly legacy IS applications, is spread throughout the system—in the database, in the application, and in the interface. Hierarchical databases, like IMS, spread semantics very differently from relational databases, like DB2. Data migration tools cannot capture and migrate all the semantics, since they don't access the entire system (e.g., they don't analyze applications). However, this discussion only touches the surface of the problem of semantics. The issue is covered in more detail in Chapter 8.

The available tools for interface migration are relatively simple to use, but they do not provide a lot of the benefits of client/server. Migrating the applications adds benefits by offloading more processing from the mainframe, but the problem is still accessing the data on the mainframe. The choice of middleware to access legacy databases is an alternative, but it is not without some time commitment. Ultimately the best option is reengineering legacy data to modern database technology, and, no matter what tool you choose, this process will be no small task.

10.2.4 Testing

A thorough test phase identifies the amount of unit and integration testing needed to turn over your migration project. A good testing process is one that tests the most amount of logic using the least amount of data. If the target IS should be functionally equivalent to the legacy IS, a complete set of regression testing compares test paths through the new system with those of the original tested system. Performance monitoring should take place early in the process of testing the target environment, so that any problems are uncovered as early as possible.

Despite the existence of testing tools, testing usually suffers because of deadline pressure. Testing takes place at the end of a project. If that project has fallen behind schedule along the way, testing is cut short to make up lost time. It's an obvious target and often the only available one. Many projects complete without an adequate amount of testing. However, this can be one of the major benefits of Chicken Little. Since migration is in increments, testing involves just the increment. The test effort is proportional to the increment size. Testing, like everything else in Chicken Little, is done incrementally.

Many testing tools are available for multiple platforms. These products possess relatively short learning curves. In general, these tools have graphical interfaces, or PC components that do. The tools are interactive and allow for easy manipulation of testing functions like breakpoints and data values.

Testing tools do little to help with the generation of test beds or the identification of adequate test coverage—two very important elements in a migration testing plan. If a legacy IS is migrated to a target environment with functionality remaining the same, it is difficult to pinpoint the proper amount of testing to determine identical functionality. One cautionary note is that testing in distributed environments is at a much earlier stage of development and maturity than testing in mainframe systems. What is least mature is testing of aspects that involve distribution (e.g., distributed data, function, and execution).

10.2.5 Configuration Management Tools

Configuration management products provide management-enabling capabilities for migration projects. These tools can prevent disaster when multiple developers are working in parallel, as is often the case during a migration. The management features of these tools include version management, configuration building, synchronization, and auditing. They enable the management of revisions to system elements, and an audit trail tracks the changes made. Through configuration builders, systems are automatically built using the correct version of system components.

Tools in this category should be used in every Chicken Little step. Because the migration proceeds in increments, you need enhanced controls for versioning and configuration management. Multiple versions of interface and application components exist in both the legacy and target environments. This dictates rigid check-in, check-out policies for test and production programs and interfaces. The process also demands the timely and well-managed migration of components. Configuration management tools provide a wide range of documentation and version control facilities for the appropriate object management and status review of the entire project. This category completes with the production turnover and backout components for final system sign-off.

As important as these tools can be during a migration project, they do not automate every step of configuration management. You can't install a configuration management tool and expect it to take over. Some manual intervention is still required. In some instances, a configuration problem may only be found after reviewing audit logs, and that may be too late.

10.2.6 Full-Service Migration Consultants

Full-service migration consultants offer reengineering services in addition to tools. They can provide you with expert consultants with their own defined methodology framework and tools that support the framework. They might

171

propose that you use a mixture of their own tools, or they might provide of list of preferred tools from a variety of vendors. Full-service migration consultants can be hired for initial strategic planning and project setup only, or they can be hired to handle the migration in its entirety.

A portion of these reengineering service and tool providers are hardware vendors such as IBM or DEC, who offer their services and products to port existing applications onto their platforms. The rest are Big 6 consulting firms or other management consulting firms that specialize in reengineering services. Table 10.1 lists some full-service migration consultants.

Vendor	Location	
Andersen Consulting	Chicago, IL	(800) 541-7512
Cambridge Technology Partners	Cambridge, MA	(617) 374-9800
Coopers & Lybrand	Seattle, WA	(206) 622-8700
Denkart	Brussels, Belgium	32 3 866 0022
Digital Equipment Corp.		(800) 832-6277
Electronic Data Systems	Plano, TX	(214) 604-6000
IBM	Armonk, NY	(800) 860-2407
James Martin & Co.	Reston, VA	(703) 620-9504
Kelly Computer Systems	Mountain View, CA	(415) 960-1010
Nolan, Norton & Co.	Boston, MA	(617) 723-8800
Price Waterhouse	New York, NY	(212) 819-5000
Rhone Valley Systems	Geneva, Switzerland	41 22 796 0277
SPR, Inc.	Chicago, IL	(800) 777-6651

TABLE 10.1 Full-service migration consultants.

With project outsourcing, you don't have to burden your staff or hire new staff to undertake the project. If the project requires an increase in staff, you don't have to maintain the same staff level after project completion. Also, relying on experts with IS migration experience can be a great benefit. It saves you the time and cost of training your own staff in using similar methods and tools.

The experience of consultants comes at a high price. This is not to imply that it isn't worth the cost. You must weigh the benefits of using consultants who have experience against the alternative of using your own staff. You might consider using a mixture of consultants and your own staff. The consultants' expertise may certainly pay off early in project planning and start-up.

A recent multimillion-dollar lawsuit against an IT consulting firm has brought to light the worst aspects of outsourcing significant IT projects. The company initiating this suit advises others to monitor outsourced projects closely and be directly involved.

The tools that full-service vendors offer are a mixture from the five tool categories. These tools have the same limitations and benefits already discussed. Although they may be strong in some aspects, they will not cover every migration step. It will still be necessary to perform some steps manually. The steps that no tools cover thoroughly are discussed in more detail in Section 10.3.

10.3 TOOLS AND THE CHICKEN LITTLE STEPS

In this section, each Chicken Little step in discussed in terms of possible tool support. A series of tables list available products, including vendor information and brief descriptions of each product.

The Chicken Little Steps

1. Incrementally analyze the legacy IS.
2. Incrementally decompose the legacy IS structure.
3. Incrementally design the target interfaces.
4. Incrementally design the target applications.
5. Incrementally design the target database.
6. Incrementally install the target environment.
7. Incrementally create and install the necessary gateways.
8. Incrementally migrate the legacy database.
9. Incrementally migrate the legacy applications.
10. Incrementally migrate the legacy interfaces.
11. Incrementally cut over to the target IS.

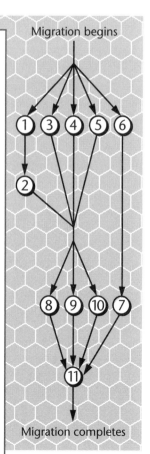

173

Step 1: Incrementally Analyze the Legacy IS

The first step in legacy IS migration is understanding application and data functionality. As Brodie and Stonebraker state in Chapter 1, we assume that your target system will include a significant portion of legacy data and function. Although legacy information systems support day-to-day business operations, the specifics of how they function are hidden. In the majority of cases, documentation is either nonexistent or out-of-date. The process of extracting or creating suitable documentation is a labor-intensive task. The help of application analyzers, both data and procedure, can help to decrease this cost, but they do not generate this information automatically. Analyzing tools currently on the market document logic flow, but they really don't do much in terms of demonstrating application functionality. In specific cases, it may be practical to custom-write programs that extract specifications from legacy code. These types of tools go a long way in helping to document modules in the process of being rewritten.

At an application level, analyzers and data repository products provide impact analysis information for an entire application. To document application flow, they cross-reference entities such as JCL to object modules and program modules. To document data flow, these products provide documentation of existing relationships for data definitions to associated copybooks, files, and databases. Besides documenting relationships or similarities, they also highlight anomalies. For the procedural, these conditions can range from potentially dangerous situations, such as active object modules with no associated source module, to poor quality, such as obsolete programs or data. On the data relationship side, cross-reference documentation identifies data redundancies and aliases. If you use these tools early in the migration process to highlight problems, they can be fixed before modules are migrated to the target IS.

Application analyzers also provide a variety of metrics demonstrating application complexity. These statistics pinpoint difficulty rating in implementing modifications, and they are a base of measurement in determining project hours and costs.

The program-level analyzing tools aid navigation through complex program logic. The tools feature tracing of program logic at the paragraph level, which allows a user to quickly scan inserted documentation for easier program comprehension. These tools trace all possible logical execution paths, or they can trace execution flow according to specific data values, demonstrating the movement forward or backward from any point in the program. With these features they can highlight unexecutable, fall through, and recursive logic areas, as well as unused data items. The resulting documentation reports are either viewed on-line or printed in a batch report.

Database analysis tools extract data structures from legacy ISs. These tools place the extracted information in an intermediate model. From this model, you can make modifications or additions so the model most accurately reflects your business. These products help in reengineering flat or hierarchical structures to a relational format.

The tools in this category typically reside in a suite of framework products that incorporates analysis at application, program, database, and file levels. Most of the application analyzers execute in the background as static analyzers, but some of the dynamic analyzers have incorporated features into their framework suite to dynamically view information at an application level. Be cautious, however, of the resources required for on-line products to analyze at an application level.

Table 10.2 identifies the tool options that aid in the automation of this first Chicken Little step. Some incorporate all of the pieces we discussed, whereas others focus specifically on one area, either data or procedure. None of these tools automatically extracts specifications from legacy code. However, they do provide documentation where it was originally obsolete or nonexistent. These tools can also be useful after project completion, when they can be applied to everyday maintenance tasks.

Step 2: Incrementally Decompose the Legacy IS Structure

Brodie and Stonebraker advocate gradual migration in small incremental steps to reach your desired goals. This strategy is easiest when your legacy IS can be decomposed. Otherwise you must identify functions that you can rewrite on the target side. The level to which decomposition can occur determines which Chicken Little migration method you follow. To research these links of separation between interface modules, procedure calls, and database services, the same tools mentioned in step 1 for application analysis can be used. See the application analyzers in Table 10.2.

The application analyzers and data repository tools produce graphics and charts illustrating application flow, along with program and data dependencies. The documentation cross-references programs that use specific copybooks, files, databases, and data elements. The impact analysis capabilities can report on a program or data change and its subsequent effect. If a logical break exists where the least amount of interference will occur to the database or other programs within the system, these tools aid in determining its existence.

Product	Vendor	Description
Application and database analyzers		
Battlemap, Codebreaker, and Instrumentation	McCabe & Associates, Inc. Columbia, MD (800) 638-6316	Documents code and structure; identifies and associates modules and system architecture
COBOL SF and ReDiscovery	IBM Armonk, NY (800) 860-2407	Restructures COBOL code and manages the reuse of legacy applications into new environments
DataTec	Compuware Corp. Farmington Hills, MI (800) 547-4000	Assists in the normalization of data element names across databases
DCD III	Marble Computer Martinsburg, WV (304) 267-1400	Provides documentation and analysis of COBOL programs aimed at reducing maintenance costs
Ensemble	Cadre Technologies Providence, RI (401) 351-5950	Helps C developers gain a quick understanding of code and automatically generates documentation
Existing Systems Workbench (ESW)	VIASOFT Phoenix, AZ (800) 525-7775	Designed to automate the process of maintaining legacy COBOL systems
Legacy Workbench	KnowledgeWare Atlanta, GA (800) 444-8575	Analyzes COBOL code quality, restructures programs, and identifies business logic for reuse
Maintenance Workbench	Intersolv Rockville, MD (800) 252-1400	Client/server environment for system-level analysis
PATHVU, RETROFIT, and XPEDITER+	Compuware Corp. Farmington Hills, MI (800) 547-4000	System-wide analysis, code restructuring, and interactive testing
Revolve	Micro Focus Palo Alto, CA (800) 872-6265	Provides system-wide data impact analysis along with other system- and program-level analysis features

Table continued on next page

Product	Vendor	Description
Specification extractors		
Design Recovery	Intersolv Rockville, MD (800) 252-1400	Extracts design information that can be loaded into Intersolv's Excelerator
Fast Forward	Seer Technology Cary, NC (919) 380-5000	Translates legacy systems by extracting process and data definitions into Seer's HPS client/server development environment
NorthStar	KnowledgeWare Atlanta, GA (800) 444-8575	Leverages investment in systems by allowing the capture of procedure routines and data
Database repositories		
Brownstone	BrownStone Solutions New York, NY (800) 627-7001	Defines and maintains system objects and generates documentation on their relationships
DB/Excel	RelTech Inc. Arlington, VA (703) 812-8000	Used for data model management or as a data dictionary
PM/SS, System Vision Year 2000	Adpac San Francisco, CA (415) 777-5400	Extracts data attribute information and helps to estimate the size of century compliant projects

TABLE 10.2 Application and database analyzers, specification extractors, and database repositories.

More recent tools address the specific tasks of system decomposition. These tools have evolved as a result of the popularity of client/server migration. Their purpose is to identify logical breakpoints between the client and server portions within an application. They operate by broadly assessing the impact of changes as a result of partitioning an application. Further documentation details the resulting effects on data and other programs. These tools usually operate under the premise that the selected portion will be migrated into a distributed environment, with some portions remaining on the mainframe. However, the tools can also support the incremental migration of an entire application to a client/server environment.

These tools provide some assistance over manual mechanisms. With large-scale systems, this can be a significant help. The best dependency tool would guarantee that any modification to program *A* will not have an effect on another program *B*. This tool does not exist today. It requires the use of analysis tools in combination with a large amount of manual effort to deduce that result. The same tools that help with analyzing legacy structure also help for decomposing legacy systems. See Table 10.2 for specific database analyzer information. The dependency features within these tools are really only used for migration projects. Their use is less likely for everyday maintenance.

Step 3: Incrementally Design the Target Interfaces

A graphical interface gives new life to existing applications. The implementation of these newborn front ends facilitates the transition of legacy ISs into distributed environments by maintaining a link to the existing mainframe applications and databases. This process completely supports the incremental nature of Brodie and Stonebraker's Chicken Little strategy. The design and implementation of target interfaces is a logical step in starting this incremental transition.

The first front-end products introduced were known as screen scrappers. These products served their function of initial transition, but now this technology has advanced to provide better options. The new tools replace the character screens by generating a graphical replacement. The products accept as input the present character image and generate a "first cut" as a graphical image. Further enhancement of these generated images can then be made via editing functions. The continuous refinement is a process of visual placement of object images that represent elements such as list and scroll boxes. The underlying functions of the interface can also be modified through the interface's scripting language. External calls trigger messages to initiate mainframe or distributed applications. Some products also pass data and initiate external applications through the use of dynamic data exchange.

When evaluating your available options for interface design and incremental migration, keep in mind ease of use, connectivity, and portability. The graphical interface generators should be straightforward and relatively easy to use. Interface modifications are basically point-and-click movements to place screen elements. The interface tool you choose should support at a minimum the target and legacy platforms with relative ease. It should also provide simultaneous connections to the legacy and target databases and applications. See Table 10.3 for client/server migration tools that have interface generation capabilities; also see the application and IS gateway products listed in Table 10.4.

Product	Vendor	Description
Application migration products		
ADW	KnowledgeWare/Sterling Software Atlanta, GA (800) 444-8575	Application development environment for numerous applications, including client/server
ClientBuilder	ClientSoft, Inc. Tarrytown, NY (800) 622-2684	Client-based application development environment used to reengineer AS/400 and mainframe-based applications to client/server
Client/Server Ready	Cognos Corp. Burlington, MA (800) 426-4667	Product and service offering that migrates midrange platforms to client/server computing
COBOL SoftBench	Hewlett Packard Palo Alto, CA (800) 752-0900	Eases the migration of legacy COBOL applications to UNIX
Composer by IEF	Texas Instruments Plano, TX (800) 336-5236	Model-driven application development tools that run in a client/server environment
FBE	Digital Equipment Corp. (800) 832-6277	Application integration capability
Informix-SE	Informix Software Menlo Park, CA (415) 926-6300	An SQL wrapper than supports an incremental migration
Micro Focus Workbench	Micro Focus, Inc. Palo Alto, CA (800) 872-6265	Offloads development, testing, and production of mainframe applications
Huron ObjectStar	Antares Alliance Group Dallas, TX (214) 447-5500	An integrated application development and execution environment
PowerBuilder	PowerSoft Burlington, MA (800) 273-2841	Supports client/server development in a Windows environment
Seer HPS	Seer Technologies, Inc. Cary, NC (919) 380-5000	Client/server application development environment
Smartpath	Dun & Bradstreet Software Atlanta, GA (404) 239-2000	Consists of four comp o-nents for client/server migration

Table continued on next page

Product	Vendor	Description
Application migration products, continued		
SQL Windows	Gupta Corp. Menlo Park, CA (800) 876-3267	Client/server application development environment
Uniface	Compuware Farmington Hills, MI (800) 547-4000	Client/server development platform supporting multiple platforms, including OS/2, UNIX, Windows, and Macintosh
VisualAge and ReDiscovery	IBM Armonk, NY (800) 860-2407	Packages code identified by ReDiscovery into objects that can be reused in client/server applications
Visual Basic	Microsoft Redmond, WA (800) 426-9400	Client/server application development environment
Database migration products		
Analyst Capture DBA Database Designer Reengineering Product Set	Bachman Information Systems Burlington, MA (800) 222-4626	Transforms existing database designs, for example, from IMS to DB2
Convert Series	Forecross Corp. San Francisco, CA (415) 543-1515	Provides the complete migration of programs, schemas, data, and other components to a new database platform
Cross Access	Cross Access Oak Brook, IL (708) 954-0500	Provides remote access to relational and nonrelational legacy systems
Data Extractor Tool (DXT)	IBM Armonk, NY (800) 860-2407	Extracts legacy data and manages its distribution to a new database platform
DataTec	Compuware Corp. Farmington Hills, MI (800) 547-4000	Assists in the normalization of data element names across databases

Table continued on next page

Product	Vendor	Description
Database migration products, continued		
DBStar Migration Architect	DBStar, Inc. San Francisco, CA (415) 512-0300	Automates data modeling, data reengineering, and legacy data migration
Design Recovery	Intersolv Rockville, MD (800) 252-1400	Extracts data structures into Intersolv's Excelerator II product
Enterprise/Access Enterprise/Sync	Apertus Technologies Eden Prairie, MN (612) 828-0300	Development environment that creates a transparent interface to legacy applications and databases during migration
Extract Tool Suite	Evolutionary Technologies, Inc. Austin, TX (512) 327-6994	Automates the distribution of data
InfoPump InfoHub	Trinzic Redwood City, CA (415) 591-8200	Performs data transfer between relational databases; provides SQL access to legacy nonrelational and relational databases
Integrity	Vality Technology, Inc. Boston, MA (617) 338-0300	Automates data cleanup by locating and correcting data anomalies
Legacy Data Mover (LDM)	Legent Corp. Herndon, VA (800) 676-5468	Manages the distribution of data to a new database platform
LoadPlus	BMC Software Houston, TX (713) 918-8800	Loads data into the target database
OEC Data Access	Open Environment Corp. Boston, MA (617) 499-1632	Wraps legacy databases and attaches them to new client/server applications
Pangaea Model	Telos Corp. Herndon, VA (703) 471-6000	Links data in legacy databases with an object-oriented DBMS
Interface migration products		
Dialog 3270 Feature of Micro Focus Dialog System	Micro Focus Palo Alto, CA (800) 872-6265	Automatically front-ends applications with a graphical interface

Table continued on next page   **181**

Product	Vendor	Description
Interface migration products, continued		
Enfin	Easel Burlington, MA (617) 221-2100	Provides front-end graphical images for client/server applications
FlashPoint	KnowledgeWare Atlanta, GA (800) 444-8575	Creates graphical interfaces for host applications and integrates multiple applications on the desktop
Mozart Composer	Mozart Systems Burlingame, CA (415) 340-1588	Generates the graphical user interface, including all of the interface logic

TABLE 10.3 Migration products.

Product	Vendor	Description
Database gateways		
Database Gateway for DB2 & DB2-CICS Access Server	Micro-Decisionware Boulder, CO (303) 443-2706	A two-part database gateway: one for the LAN-based server and one for the mainframe
EDA/SQL	Information Builders, Inc. New York, NY (212) 736-4433	Database-independent on both client and server components, providing transparent access to over 50 DBMSs
Enterprise Connect	Sybase Emeryville, CA (800) 879-2273	Doesn't require Sybase's DBMS; transmits data requests to over 20 databases, including IMS
Gupta/SQLHost	Gupta Menlo Park, CA (415) 321-9500	Links Gupta C/S applications with DB2 and/or other mainframe DBMSs
Informix Gateway	Informix Software, Inc. Menlo Park, CA (415) 926-6300	Transparently accesses and modifies legacy databases
Ingres/Gateway	Ingres Alameda, CA (510) 769-1400	Links the Ingres database with DB2 and/or other mainframe DBMSs

Table continued on next page

Product	Vendor	Description
Database gateways, continued		
Micro Focus COBOL/SQL Transparency System	Micro Focus Palo Alto, CA (800) 872-6265	Enables applications to access relational databases using standard COBOL I/O syntax
SQL*Connect SQL*Net	Oracle Redwood Shores, CA (415) 506-7000	Links the Oracle database with DB2 and/or other mainframe DBMSs
Platinum Integrator	Platinum Technology Oak Brook Terrace, IL (800) 442-6861	Enables access to legacy mainframe data from a client/server environment without rewriting any application code
Transparency	Computer Associates Islandia, NY (516) 342-5224	Enables the access of existing database I/O to CA-Datacom
XDB	XDB Systems, Inc. Laurel, MD (301) 317-6800	A PC database where DB2 applications can easily share data between the PC and mainframe
Application and IS gateways		
Copernicus	New Paradigm Software New York, NY (212) 557-0933	Translates system transactions and functions between legacy and distributed application components
Enfin	Easel Burlington, MA (617) 221-2100	Provides front-end graphical images for client/server applications
FlashPoint	KnowledgeWare Atlanta, GA (800) 444-8575	Creates graphical interfaces for host applications and integrates multiple applications on the desktop
Mozart Composer	Mozart Systems Burlingame, CA (415) 340-1588	Generates the graphical user interface, including all of the interface logic
TransAccess	Netwise Boulder, CO (303) 442-8280	Provides access to and from legacy systems, including IMS/DC and CICS

TABLE 10.4 Gateway products.

183

Step 4: Incrementally Design the Target Applications

Previous chapters identify the distinction between functionality and code, because much of the code is dispensable or replaceable. On the other hand, most or all of the functionality will be repeated from the legacy to the target applications. Even if you choose to leave portions of the legacy applications intact, what you do migrate to the target platform will be functionally equivalent to its legacy counterpart.

The focus then in designing the new target applications will be on functional specifications. The data model extracted from earlier Chicken Little steps will also be important because the legacy data must be preserved as well as the legacy functionality. The design of the target applications, therefore, is based on a continual review of the extracted data model and functional specifications.

The tools for designing target applications can be either an integrated toolset that includes design and generation capabilities, such as a CASE tool, or independent design tools with an application generator. Some of these products are listed in Table 10.3. Many of the CASE or independent modeling tools provide a bridge to client/server development products. However, links between tools have never really worked well. At their best performance, you can convert just a small amount of the completed design.

Step 5: Incrementally Design the Target Database

Legacy databases tend to be ill-structured and contain a significant number of problems. These conditions stem from years of no standards in data definitions and repeated maintenance patching. Databases also tend to contain vast amounts of data. From working with TPS at Global Telecom and CMS at Money Central, Brodie and Stonebraker believe that a considerable amount of this data is obsolete and need not be migrated. They see a real benefit for automated products that extract, repair, validate, and translate data in the process from legacy to target ISs. A growing number of products support portions of these data-scrubbing features; see Table 10.3 for more information.

The lack or absence of database standards and separate database responsibilities in older systems has led to a tight integration between legacy data and code. Old systems have few if any databases—usually they are a mixture of VSAM or flat files. Their definitions tend to be distributed throughout the code and often are not distinguishable from the application code. This makes the process of extracting data specifications for new database designs extremely difficult. To add complexity to the design problem, database migration software requires the manual definition of a migration schema. The migration schema provides a mapping of the legacy database to the target database. In using these tools, Brodie and Stonebraker saw the need for added functionality. They felt that the tools would be much more useful if they could assist with analyzing data definitions in the legacy IS and the design of the migration schema. The most that existing products provide in the automatic mapping between two schemas are suggestions, based on simple text matching of the data element names, that a data element in one schema matches an element in another schema.

Table 10.3 lists tools that you can use to design a target database. If you are already using a tool to extract the legacy database models, that product probably has an environment to design a new target model using the legacy data. The Bachman product line is the pioneer in this particular area of reengineering database design. They are best known for their ability to take legacy databases and restructure them through a series of steps into a new relational structure.

If your process of extracting the legacy database model was manual or through custom programs, you can use any number of database design tools to now create a new database model. A few of these PC-based design tools have created links to the more popular client/server development products. Although a bridge function is a nice feature to eliminate redundancy, these functions have never worked the best, and usually the process is never able to transmit all the defined data models and definitions.

Step 6: Incrementally Install the Target Environment

No specific tools are available to help you install the target environment, other than the tool's own internal installation process. Tools are available, however, that help to benchmark target performance. These report on resource utilization and performance statistics. These utilities will become even more useful once incremental migration begins.

Step 7: Incrementally Create and Install the Necessary Gateways

The LAN-to-mainframe connectivity market is moving toward providing an environment that accommodates both distributed and

185

mainframe resources. Its composition allows organizations to incorporate distributed components into their existing enterprise architectures. The gateway functionality is what Brodie and Stonebraker refer to as a surround technology (the term *wrappers* is also used in this regard). For example, their experience with the CMS case study was creating an environment that would seamlessly move VSAM files to DBMS technology. In order to properly match all your present and future distributed gateway requirements, a number of questions should be addressed before implementation.

Does the gateway support the databases, interfaces, communications, and any other major system components? It is extremely beneficial for the gateway technology to encapsulate all of these elements. Since one gateway product may not meet all of your requirements, Brodie and Stonebraker suggest that any development or enhancements of gateway products be done with systems experts, especially those trained in the area of transaction processing. Since it is unlikely that vendors other than DBMS or TP monitor vendors have such expertise, there are a few other available alternatives. One solution is to contract with a gateway vendor to enhance their gateway functionality to accommodate all of your requirements. If this does not become a viable option because of the amount of changes, another alternative is to contract to have the gateway built for you by a DBMS or TP monitor expert. If the above alternatives fail, a last resort is to build the gateway yourself, only after fully understanding its requirements.

The function of a gateway imposes stringent performance requirements. Their interaction between two critical ISs must meet or exceed user expectations. As a rule of thumb, Brodie and Stonebraker suggest not imposing more than a 10% performance degradation from the current legacy IS. How this level of performance should be achieved is not always a simple answer. The process of choosing or enhancing the right gateway product for your organization improves chances for better performance.

A very large number of gateway products exist. Table 10.4 divides the products into the previously defined types of database, IS, and application gateways. The IS and application gateways are grouped together because some products serve both functions. The database gateways include DBMS vendors that have products connecting the distributed databases to mainframe legacy databases. The category also includes database-independent vendors like Micro-Decisionware and Information Builders, who provide access to multiple distributed and mainframe databases.

Step 8: Incrementally Migrate the Legacy Database

By the time you reach this step, the target database has been selected and implemented. Now it's important to perform a thorough job of data reengineering. This procedure attempts to diminish the multiple data contaminants that have spread through years of continuously defining data elements. If left alone, these inaccuracies propagate not only to the new database but to all systems and repositories that interact with these sources. These past problems may compound problems with the new systems.

Data reengineering tools transform legacy data to attain a higher data quality. Data from multiple DBMSs are input and undergo a thorough investigation and standardization process. Results uncover misspellings, multiple fields, repetitive values, and unusual data definitions. These steps are not a small task for the large volumes of data that exist in legacy databases. In fact, we estimate that data scrubbing cost in and of itself may prevent some large migration projects from starting or, if started, from ever concluding. True cost estimates for data scrubbing are hard to make and, if accurate, are almost never believed by management because of their enormous size.

The final step in data migration transports the reengineered data to the new database. Several tools are available that convert or assist in the process of moving data to a new DBMS.

An option is available for those who would like to receive the immediate benefits of new technology while migrating legacy data. Middleware software transparently links distributed applications to the existing mainframe databases. A middleware solution allows the development of client/server applications before completing the large initial investment to reengineer databases. Their services process the transactions to multiple distributed and mainframe databases. The same remote procedural calls from a client application access both relational and legacy databases. A word of caution about these products: the initial data mapping that these products require is time consuming, and there is no automated way to perform this procedure.

Data reengineering, data transport, and middleware tools are found within Table 10.3, under database migration. See the tool descriptions to identify whether their purpose is to transform design, identify redundancies, automate data cleanup, or transport data to a new database. The middleware products that allow access to legacy databases while in the process of migrating to a new database are also listed here.

Step 9: Incrementally Migrate the Legacy Applications

The tools to incrementally migrate portions of the legacy applications operate in a variety of ways. Some of them download portions of the application to be recompiled and implemented in the target environment using the same language, typically COBOL. Others analyze the legacy system and partition it into components for migration to a target environment such as client/server. Some even attempt to extract a portion of the business functions for reimplementation.

From Brodie and Stonebraker's experience, you will not be able to migrate any of the legacy code. Instead, they believe it will be necessary to rewrite the application in a client/server development environment. It might, however, be feasible to rewrite a component of the application for client/server that accesses other components still on the mainframe. This role will be a function of the mainframe gateway, adding an extra layer to its complexity.

The tools for application migration are listed in Table 10.3. They include a range of products like the PC COBOL Micro Focus and CA-Realia products to others like Visual Basic and Uniface that generate new client/server applications. You can also find products that extract legacy specifications for regeneration in a client/server environment, such as KnowledgeWare's NorthStar, under specification extractors in Table 10.2. These products are much more complex and have not been as successful as rewriting in a new client/server language.

Step 10: Incrementally Migrate the Legacy Interfaces

When rewriting the application in a client/server language, the interface migration may or may not occur in parallel with the application migration. Whether it does or not is determined by the dependence of the application components. Client/server application development products provide for an integrated platform to develop both interfaces and applications. On the other hand, products that strictly generate graphical interfaces can leave the majority of business functions in the legacy environment, replacing the character screen with a graphical image. A third alternative are interface products that provide terminal emulation and mainframe connectivity for controlling 3270 sessions.

With the wide array of interface generation products, the challenge will be which alternative to choose. The interface tool decision needs to coordinate with the choice of application development tool. If a client/server development product is the direction, then the interface tool will fall into that one integrated environment. If, however, you have chosen to use a separate interface tool to provide incremental interface migration, most of these tools provide interfaces to communicate with other application components. This is accomplished via some form of remote procedural calls. See Table 10.3 for a breakdown of interface and application migration products.

Step 11: Incrementally Cut Over to the Target IS

Testing and application turnover are two areas that frequently are overlooked. Projects typically run close to or over budget and schedule, and as a result these final procedures are rushed. Many testing tools are available that perform a variety of functions from dynamically testing applications to identifying test coverage. The majority of these tools are mainframe COBOL-based products. The client/server development tools typically provide their own environment for testing.

In a large distributed network, a Cold Turkey migration from legacy to target environment is unrealistic. With Chicken Little, Brodie and Stonebraker outline a graceful way to move to a target environment while allowing the IS to continuously operate. Their suggested method, along with the available tools, supports a smooth, incremental cutover from legacy to target IS. A well-planned testing environment can assist in this smooth transition.

The list of tools in Table 10.5 may already exist in your everyday work environment. These tools provide various interactive test capabilities and identify statistics such as amount of code coverage in the mainframe legacy ISs.

In testing a project that is migrating function, an essential step is to ensure that the system functionality has not changed. This phase of testing is called regression testing. In order to do an adequate job of regression testing, you must identify from the legacy system the amount of code coverage and test data that is necessary. The mainframe tools in Table 10.5 will assist in making these determinations.

Product	Vendor	Description
CA-Intertest	Computer Associates Islandia, NY (516) 342-5224	Mainframe-based; assists in regression testing of migration projects
CA-Realia COBOL Workbench	Computer Associates Islandia, NY (516) 342-5224	Complete PC development environment that includes an interactive testing component for COBOL applications
McCabe Testing Toolset	McCabe & Associates Columbia, MD (800) 638-6316	Mainframe-based; helps to determine the number of tests needed and distinguish what is testable from what is not
Micro Focus COBOL Workbench	Micro Focus Palo Alto, CA (800) 872-6265	Complete PC development environment that includes an interactive testing component for COBOL applications
Xpediter	Compuware Corp. Farmington Hills, MI (800) 547-4000	Interactive mainframe code analyzer that allows the user to trace logic paths during execution and assists in the regression test functions of legacy IS migration

TABLE 10.5 Testing products.

10.4 MIGRATION MANAGEMENT

Legacy IS migration is a complicated, complex process. Properly planning and managing the Chicken Little steps takes a lot of thought. It's a huge challenge to select the increments to be migrated, interleave the largely independent steps, and sequence the steps to diminish risk of failure. Since all IS modules are in a state of change, many versions must be managed. This migration architecture is more complex than either the legacy or target architectures. It's also mission-critical.

This complexity requires careful management. Migration management should be fundamentally supported by an industrial-strength configuration management tool. Refer to Table 10.6 for a list of these products. Configuration management systems are designed to label components and to track the versions and configurations in which they are active. However, they are not

Product	Vendor	Description
CA-PAN/LCM	Computer Associates Islandia, NY (516) 342-5224	Manages development and maintenance projects, with features for change and configuration management
Endevor	Legent Corp. Herndon, VA (800) 676-5468	Automates the management of the entire development process from initial design to distribution
Maestro	Softlab Atlanta, GA (404) 668-8811	Supports redevelopment projects by integrating people, process, and tools
Process Engineer	LBMS, Inc. Houston, TX (800) 231-7515	Provides interactive process management
PVCS	Intersolv Rockville, MD (800) 252-1400	Deploys an integrated family of software configuration management tools designed for LAN-based team development

TABLE 10.6 Project management products.

specifically designed to support an incremental strategy for identifying and managing migration increments, configuration, and versions. This is a significant piece of work and a key management activity throughout the life of the project.

10.5 GETTING STARTED

A comprehensive understanding of the entire migration process, as opposed to an understanding of the individual steps, is the key to beginning a successful legacy IS migration. This process-oriented view helps to conceive, manage, and ultimately control the migration and to identify resources, such as tools, that will be critical to your success.

Clearly understand your project objectives before beginning any of the Chicken Little steps. When making tool choices, select those tools that work together to reach the project objectives. Keep in mind that some of your migration tools may remain in place after the project completes. When the migration architecture is set and the project is ready to begin, the tool choices should be the best available to automate the necessary steps for a successful migration project. With this foundation, you're ready to go.

191

GLOSSARY

application gateway A gateway placed between the interfaces and the target and legacy ISs. It intercepts application calls from user interfaces and GUIs and directs them to the appropriate legacy or target application module. It directs responses from the application back to the calling interface. The gateway must accomplish other tasks as well.

asynchronous transaction model Transactions are decomposed into subtransactions, and each subtransaction can commit or roll back independently of the other subtransactions.

brittle IS Any IS that is easily broken—made inoperable—when modified for any purpose.

Brooks effect When resources are added to late projects, inevitably the projects become even later.

chained transaction model Each subtransaction commits, but the failure of any subsequent subtransaction does not require the repeat of previously committed subtransactions. Only the subtransaction that has failed needs to be restarted.

Chicken Little A cautionary migration method that enables you to control risk by migrating in small, manageable increments.

Cold Turkey A massive cutover from legacy to target IS.

composite IS The IS formed during the migration, in which the legacy IS and the target IS work together to perform all mission-critical operations. The legacy and target ISs are connected by a gateway.

193

cutover The process of switching from a legacy IS component to the corresponding target IS component. Operations are cut over in increments site by site, user by user, according to specific environments.

data liberation Any application can use the DBMS to access data.

database gateway This gateway is placed between the application modules and the database service. It intercepts calls to the database service and directs them to the appropriate legacy or target database service. It directs responses back from the database service to the calling application. The gateway must accomplish other tasks also.

decomposable IS Interface, application, and database services are distinct components with well-defined interfaces. The application modules are independent of each other and interact only with the database service.

forward gateway Enables legacy applications to access a database environment on the target side of the migration process. It translates legacy calls forward to target calls.

forward migration The entire database environment is initially migrated, followed by the installation of a forward database gateway through which the legacy applications may access the target environment.

gateway A software module introduced between operation software components to mediate between them.

general migration method This method is for semidecomposable ISs. It involves a combination of both forward and reverse migration methods. The gateway is complex, functioning variously as forward gateway, reverse gateway, mapping table, and coordinator.

incremental migration Migration proceeds in chunks. Each chunk brings you closer to complete migration to the target environment.

inflexible IS An IS that is difficult to adapt to changing business needs.

IS apoplexy Condition that renders an organization helpless to expand or improve because its legacy IS monopolizes the company's resources. The company spends all its time and money trying to maintain the legacy instead of moving to cheaper, more efficient software.

IS backlog The list of current business requirements that your legacy IS cannot support.

IS gateway A gateway that encapsulates the entire legacy IS. It intercepts end-user and system interface calls and directs them to the legacy IS or some target component. It directs responses back to the calling interface. Much functionality is involved with this gateway.

jelly beans A multithreaded low-cost UNIX server that is appropriate for deploying application and interface modules.

legacy IS Any IS that is resistant to change.

mapping table Software and data that support the gateway functions by maintaining links between corresponding legacy and target components.

middleware Software that resides between the application and the platform.

mission-critical data Any data that is essential to the everyday operations of a business.

mission-critical IS IS that is needed practically 24 hours/day. The success of the business is dependent upon its performance.

nondecomposable IS No functional elements are considered separable.

portable architecture A flexible, decomposable environment.

reverse gateway Gateway that enables target applications to access the legacy data management environment. It translates target calls back into legacy calls.

reverse migration The database migration is postponed until the end of the process. When the target environment is complete except for the database, a reverse gateway is installed to permit access to the database portions awaiting migration.

rightsizing The transition from large mainframe computers to smaller, less expensive, more easily maintainable computers.

semidecomposable IS The user interfaces and system interfaces are separate modules, but the applications and database service are not separable.

successful legacy IS migration It begins with a mission-critical legacy IS in full production and ends with a fully operational, mission-critical target application (or applications components) that replaces the essential aspects of the original legacy IS.

synchronous transaction models These require 2PC or corollary protocols to ensure that all updates act as continuous, distributed transaction support for commits and rollbacks.

target environment The hardware and software of the post-migration IS.

variant record encodings The interpretation of one data element is controlled by another data element.

REFERENCES

Breibart, Y., et al. 1990. "Reliable Transaction Management in a Multi-Database System." In *Proc. 1990 ACM SIGMOD Conference on Management of Data.* New York: ACM.

Brodie, M. L. 1992. "The Promise of Distributed Computing and the Challenges of Legacy Systems." In P. M. D. Gray and R. J. Lucas, eds., *Advanced Database Systems: Proceedings of the 10th British National Conference on Databases.* New York: Springer-Verlag. Also in D. Hsiao, E. J. Neuhold, and R. Sacks-Davis, eds., *Proceedings of the IFIP TC2/WG2.6 Conference on Semantics of Interoperable Database Systems.* Amsterdam: Elsevier, 1993. Also in A. Dogac, M. T. Özsu, A. Biliris, and T. Sellis, eds., *Advances in Object-Oriented Database Systems.* New York: Springer-Verlag, 1994.

Brooks, F. 1975. *The Mythical Man-Month.* Reading, MA: Addison-Wesley.

Communications of the ACM. 1994. Vol. 37, no. 5 (May).

> Aiken, P., et al. "DoD Legacy Systems: Reverse Engineering Data Requirements."
> Biggerstaff, T., et al. "Program Understanding and the Concept Assignment Problem."
> Markosian, L., et al. "Using an Enabling Technology to Reengineer Legacy Systems."
> Ning, J., et al. "Automated Support for Legacy Code Understanding."

Premerlani, W., and Blaha, M. "An Approach for Reverse Engineering of Relational Databases."

Quilici, A. "A Memory-Based Approach to Recognizing Programming Plans."

Date, C. 1987. *Selected Readings in Database Systems*. Reading, MA: Addison-Wesley.

Elmagarmid, A. K., ed. 1992. *Database Transaction Models for Advanced Applications*. San Mateo, CA: Morgan Kaufmann.

Garcia-Molina, H., and Salem, K. 1987. "Sagas." In *Proc. 1987 ACM SIGMOD Conference on Management of Data*. New York: ACM.

Gray, J., and Reuter, A. 1993. *Transaction Processing: Concepts and Techniques*. San Mateo, CA: Morgan Kaufmann.

IEEE Software. 1995a. Vol. 12, no. 3 (March).

Sharon, D., and Bell, R. "Tools that Bind: Creating Integrated Environments."

IEEE Software. 1995b. Vol. 12, no. 1 (January).

Bennett, K. "Legacy Systems: Coping with Success."

Bray, O., and Hess, M. "Reengineering a Configuration-Management System."

Dedene, G., and De Vreese, J.-P. "Realities of Off-Shore Reengineering."

Merlo, E., et al. "Reengineering User Interfaces."

Sneed, H. "Planning the Reengineering of Legacy Systems."

Wong, K., et al. "Structural Redocumentation: A Case Study."

IEEE Software. 1992. Vol. 9, no. 3 (March).

Chen, M., and Norman, R. "A Framework for Integrated CASE."

Norman, R., and Chen, M. "Working Together to Integrate CASE."

Thomas, I., and Nejmeh, B. "Definitions of Tool Integration for Environments."

Özsu, M. T., and Valduriez, P. 1991. *Principles of Distributed Database Systems*. Englewood Cliffs, NJ: Prentice-Hall.

Skeen, D. 1982. "Non-Blocking Commit Protocols." In *Proc. 1982 ACM SIGMOD Conference on Management of Data*. New York: ACM.

Wachter, H., and Reuter, A. 1992. "The ConTract Model." In A. K. Elmagarmid, ed., *Database Transaction Models for Advanced Applications*. San Mateo, CA: Morgan Kaufmann.

INDEX

ABOUT THE AUTHORS

Michael L. Brodie is a senior staff scientist at GTE Laboratories Inc., Waltham, Massachusetts. His primary research focus is on distributed object computing. Until 1994, Dr. Brodie headed the Distributed Object Computing Department within GTE Labs' Computer and Intelligent Systems Laboratory. His research interests include next-generation computing and applications, as well as relevant emerging technologies such as distributed object computing, interoperability, cooperative information systems, database technology, artificial intelligence, programming languages, and computer communications/telecommunications. Dr. Brodie has a major concern for the social responsibility of his own work and that of computer science as a whole. He has written and spoken out on this topic for many years.

Dr. Brodie serves on several boards, including the VLDB Endowment, the ACM SIGMOD Advisory Committee, the Telecommunications Information Networking Architecture Scientific Committee (TINA), Cooperative Information Systems (CoopIS), and the International Foundation for Cooperative Information Systems (IFCIS). He has consulted to research advisory organizations of the governments of the United States, Canada, France, Italy, Germany, Colombia, Brazil, Denmark, Australia, Russia, Ukraine, and the EEC. Dr. Brodie has authored over 70 books, journal articles, and refereed conference papers. He has also given invited lectures and short courses in over 25 countries.

Michael Stonebraker is a professor of electrical engineering and computer science at the University of California, Berkeley, where he has been employed since 1971. He was one of the principal architects of the INGRES relational database management system, which was developed during the period from 1973 to 1977. Subsequently Dr. Stonebraker constructed distributed INGRES, one of the first working distributed database systems. He then turned his attention to developing a next-generation DBMS, POSTGRES, that can effectively manage not only data but objects and rules as well. POSTGRES forms one of the cornerstones of the Sequoia 2000 project, the DEC flagship research project of the 1990s for which Dr. Stonebraker is co-project director. Sequoia 2000 is striving to build a new computer environment for earth science researchers and encompasses networking, storage DBMS, and visualization activities. Currently, he is focusing on the DBMS support for visualization environments and on next-generation distributed DBMSs.

Dr. Stonebraker is a founder of INGRES Corp. (now the INGRES Products Division of ASK Computer Systems), the founder of Illustra Information Systems, Inc., a past chairman of the ACM Special Interest Group on Management of Data, and the author of many papers on DBMS technology. He lectures widely, has been the keynote speaker at several recent conferences, and was the winner of the first ACM SIGMOD innovations award in 1992.